Roseville Pottery

Price Guide No. 10

The current values in this book should be used only as a guide. They are not intended to set prices, which vary from one section of the country to another. Auction prices as well as dealer prices vary greatly and are affected by condition as well as demand. Neither the Authors nor the Publisher assumes responsibility for any losses that might be incurred as a result of consulting this guide.

Additional copies of this book may be ordered from:

COLLECTOR BOOKS
P.O. Box 3009
Paducah, Kentucky 42002-3009

@$9.95. Add $2.00 for postage and handling.

Suggested Values

The prices in this guide represent approximate low to high evaluation. Average, if indeed an average exists, is somewhere between the two. Prices vary considerably from dealer to dealer and from one locality to another. And as always, in the end, the actual selling price is judged by the buyer himself.

There are many factors which must be considered before a reasonable appraisal can be made of any particular piece of pottery. Aside from damage incurred over the years, such as chips or cracks which obviously lessen the value of a piece considerably, certain factory defects may also detract from its value. Some of these are: glazed-over chips; pieces not truly molded, leaning or otherwise slightly irregular; poorly finished mold lines; faint embossing; poor color or careless decoration. A properly repaired piece, though worth considerably less than it would be in mint condition, would no doubt attract a buyer. This is especially true with the older, rarer lines, where high prices tend to be discouraging to many collectors. Crazing is that fine network of tiny lines caused by uneven expansion or contraction between body and glaze. This is normal in moderate amounts and should not effect values unless unusually extensive.

Some shapes are more popular with collectors than others. Ewers, baskets, and covered jars bring good prices. Some collectors prefer wall pockets or hanging baskets. Generally, vases with handles have more appeal than those without. Tea sets are popular, as are tall candlesticks. Large cumbersome items which are hard to display, may not sell as well as a smaller cabinet piece.

Many collectors are willing to pay more for a marked piece than for one that is unmarked yet unmistakably Roseville. This is especially true of those with the more unusual marks and is a matter of personal preference.

Examples of the fine art pottery from the early years of production are always in demand, and present the greatest challenge to evaluate. Scarcity of line is a prime consideration. For instance, among the Rozane lines, an example of the Crystalis line would probably bring a higher price than one of comparable size in Egypto or Rozane Royal, due simply to its scarcity. By the same token a piece of Azurean would be more valuable than either the dark or light Rozane Royal, even though all are hand-painted underglaze art lines from the same period of production.

The quality of art work varied from one artist to another. Some pieces show fine detail and good color, and naturally this influences their value. Studies of animals and portraits bring higher prices than the floral designs in the Rozane Royal, and although any piece in Della Robbia is quite expensive, the gladiators and animals are at the top of the line. Artist signatures increase the value of any item, particularly if the artist is one who is well recognized.

These suggested values are for mint condition items. By "mint" we mean first quality ware with a normal amount of crazing and no serious defects. This definition may not satisfy each and every collector or dealer, but for the sake of establishing a basis from which one may begin an appraisal, this will be our standard.

Sizes have been rounded off to the nearest ½ inch. Shape numbers are included whenever possible; they may be helpful in ordering by mail. Many pieces shown in the catalogue reprint sections of the books are also designated by numbers which can be used as reference.

First Series

Page 2

    Silver Overlay, 2½" $950.00-1,110.00

Page 35, Rozane, 1900's
Row 1:
    1. Bowl, 2½", No. 927 ....$100.00-125.00
    2. Bud Vase, 4", No. 862 ....$135.00-165.00
    3. Vase, 4" $135.00-165.00
    4. Bowl, 2½", No. 927 ....$100.00-125.00
Row 2:
    1. Ewer, 11", No. 870-4.........................$300.00-350.00
    2. Commemorative Vase, 5", No. 923 ....$200.00-250.00
    3. Ewer, 7", No. 828 ....$300.00-350.00
    4. Ewer, same as #3
Row 3:
    1. Jug, 4½", No. 888 ....$200.00-225.00
    2. Pillow Vase, 9", No. 882 ....$2,850.00-3,300.00
    3. Vase, 4", No. 844 ....$100.00-125.00
Row 4:
    1. Vase, 9½", No. 821 ....$300.00-335.00
    2. Vase, 14...$350.00-450.00
    3. Vase, same as #1

Page 37, Rozane, Rozane Lights
Row 1:
    1. Vase, 4" $175.00-200.00
    2. Jug, 7"...$200.00-275.00
    3. Pitcher, 5" $250.00-300.00
    4. Paperweight......................................$250.00-300.00
    5. Ewer, 8" $175.00-200.00
    6. Tobacco jar, 6" $500.00-600.00
    7. Pitcher, 4" $150.00-200.00
Row 2:
    1. Vase, 6½" $300.00-350.00
    2. Vase, 6" $325.00-375.00
    3. Vase, 10" $300.00-400.00
    4. Pitcher, 7" $650.00-850.00
    5. Vase, 9" $300.00-350.00
    6. Vase, 8" $250.00-350.00
Row 3:
    1. Tankard, 11½" $475.00-575.00
    2. Vase, 14" $1,000.00-1,500.00
    3. Vase, 5" $140.00-170.00
    4. Vase, 16" $1,000.00-1,500.00
    5. Pillow Vase, 10"x10" $400.00-500.00

Page 39, Rozane, Rozane Royal
Row 1:
    1. Bud Vase, 8", No. 842 ....$135.00-165.00
    2. Vase, 6", No. 883..............................$200.00-225.00
    3. Vase, 9" $500.00-600.00
    4. Bud Vase, 6", No. 831 ....$100.00-150.00
    5. Urn (lid not original; refer to page 54, *Catalogue of
    Early Roseville*) $425.00-525.00
Row 2:
    1. Mug, 4½", No. 886 ....$175.00-200.00
    2. Vase, 7" $150.00-200.00
    3. Bowl, 5½" $200.00-250.00
    4. Vase, 5½", No. 853 ....$150.00-200.00

Blue Ware
    Our skepticism regarding the authenticity of Roseville's Blue Ware line continues. This piece, even though marked with a Roseville paper label (which was not used at all during the early art period), is a Weller Louwelsa shape.
Azurean
    Vase, 4½" $450.00-550.00

Cornelian
    Cracker Jar $250.00-350.00

Page 41, Rozane
    Jardiniere and Pedestal, 31"................$800.00-1,000.00

Egypto
    1. Oil Lamp, 5" $400.00-450.00
    2. Vase, 11" $400.00-450.00
    3. Compote, 9" $450.00-550.00
    4. Pitcher, 5" $275.00-325.00

Page 43, Mara
    Vase, 13½" $2,000.00-2,250.00

Mongol
Top, right:
    Vase, 15" $1,000.00-1,100.00
Bottom, left:
    1. Bowl Vase, 3" $250.00-300.00
    2. Vase, 10" $1,150.00-1,350.00
    3. Pitcher, 6½" $850.00-950.00

Crystalis
    Ewer, 7½" $1,250.00-1,400.00

Page 45, Woodland
    1. Vase, 8" $800.00-1,100.00
    2. Vase, 10" $900.00-1,200.00
    3. Vase, 9" $800.00-1,000.00

On front cover of Roseville I book
    Vase, 17"..$1,250.00-1,500.00

Fudji
    1. Vase, 9" $1,000.00-1,250.00
    2. Vase, 10" $1,100.00-1,250.00

On front cover of Roseville I book
    Vase, 9" $1,100.00-1,200.00

Page 47, Olympic
    1. Vase, 13" $2,500.00-3,000.00
    2. Tankard, 11" $2,000.00-2,400.00

Pauleo
    Vase, 20"..$1,150.00-1,250.00

Della Robbia
    Vase, 13"..$3,000.00-5,000.00

Page 49, Tourist
    Vase, 12"..$800.00-1,100.00

Matt Color
    1. Bowl, 4" $50.00-75.00
    2. Hanging Basket, 4½" $50.00-75.00
    3. Bowl, 3" $40.00-60.00

Aztec
Row 1:
    1. Pitcher, 5" $225.00-275.00
    2. Pitcher, 5½" $275.00-325.00
Row 2:
    1. Vase, 10" $250.00-350.00
    2. Lamp, 11" $275.00-325.00
    3. Vase, 9½" $250.00-300.00
    4. Vase, 8" $250.00-300.00

Matt Green
"The Gate" $65.00-95.00

Antique Matt Green
Vase, 9½" (Questionable origin)................................$125.00-175.00

Page 51, Dutch
Top:
    1. Pitcher, 9½" $200.00-225.00
    2. Mug, 5" (See Second Series, Fraternal
       Creamware) $150.00-175.00
Bottom, Row 1:
    1. Mug, 5" $85.00-95.00
    2. Soap Dish, 3", with lid......................$200.00-225.00
    3. Tobacco Jar, 5", with lid $200.00-300.00
    4. Mug, 5"..$85.00-95.00
    5. Mug, 5"..$85.00-95.00
Row 2:
    1. Pitcher and Bowl, 9", 12" dia. $550.00-750.00
    2. Pitcher, 11" $250.00-350.00
    3. Tankard, 11½" $150.00-200.00

Creamware with Cherry Decal
Chocolate Pot, 10" $250.00-350.00

Page 53, Stein Sets
    1. Mug, 5"...$135.00-150.00
    2. Tankard, 11½" $225.00-325.00
    3. Mug, 6½".......................................$250.00-350.00
    4. Tankard, 11½" $225.00-325.00
    5. Mug, 5"...$125.00-150.00

Plate 32
    1. Ashtray, "Reyam Club Whiskey" $50.00-75.00
    2. Quaker Mug, 5".............................$145.00-175.00
    3. Ash Tray, "K of P" $50.00-75.00

Decorated and Gold Traced
Candlestick, 9"...$100.00-150.00

Gold Traced
Candlestick, 9"...$100.00-150.00

Page 52, Forget-Me-Not
Dresser Set..$250.00-300.00

Page 55, Carnelian
Row 1:
    1. Candleholder, 3", pr $50.00-75.00
    2. Candleholder, 3", pr $50.00-75.00
    3. Vase, 6"...$40.00-65.00
    4. Loving Cup Vase, 5" $55.00-85.00
    5. Flower Holder, 6" $35.00-60.00
    6. Candleholder, 2½" $30.00-40.00
Row 2:
    1. Urn, 8"..$150.00-200.00
    2. Ewer, 15"....................................$200.00-300.00
    3. Console Bowl, 14".........................$100.00-150.00
Row 3:
    1. Vase, 5"...$50.00-75.00
    2. Vase, 7".......................................$100.00-150.00
    3. Vase,10".....................................$125.00-200.00
    4. Vase, 9".....................................$125.00-175.00
    5. Fan Vase, 8" $85.00-120.00

Page 57, Mostique
    1. Vase, 6"...$50.00-85.00
    2. Vase, 10"....................................$125.00-175.00
    3. Jardiniere, 10"..............................$175.00-275.00
    4. Bowl, 2½".......................................$50.00-75.00

    5. Vase, 6"...$50.00-85.00
Imperial 1
Row 1:
    1. Basket, 6".....................................$100.00-150.00
    2. Basket, 6".....................................$100.00-150.00
    3. Vase, 8".......................................$125.00-175.00
    4. Triple Bud Vase, 8"........................$125.00-175.00
    5. Basket, 8".....................................$125.00-225.00
    6. Basket, 6".....................................$100.00-150.00
Row 2:
    1. Basket, 11"...................................$150.00-250.00
    2. Vase, 10"....................................$175.00-250.00
    3. Bud Vase, 12" $125.00-200.00
    4. Basket, 13"...................................$150.00-250.00

Page 58
Ceramic Planter with Liner, 6½"x4" $95.00-110.00

Page 59
    1.Jardiniere (shown without liner; identified on page 30,
    Catalogue of Early Roseville, as Ceramic, 4")................$85.00-95.00
    2. Wall Pocket, Persian type $250.00-300.00
    3. Wall Pocket, Ceramic Design
    (See Second Series for distinction) $250.00-300.00

Medallion
Dresser Set..$250.00-300.00

Early Pitchers
    1. Landscape, 7½" $125.00-175.00
    2. Tulip, 7½" $125.00-175.00

Dealer Signs
    1. Sign, 4½"x10" $700.00-900.00
    2. Sign, 5"x8" $700.00-800.00
    3. Sign, 2"x6" $400.00-500.00

Page 61, Landscape
    1. Covered Sugar, 3½"..........................$60.00-70.00
    2. Planter, 4½"....................................$65.00-75.00
    3. Creamer, 3"....................................$60.00-70.00

Decorated Utility Ware
    1. Pitcher, 6".......................................$50.00-75.00
    2. Pitcher, 7".......................................$50.00-75.00
    3. Pitcher, 7".......................................$50.00-75.00
    4. Pitcher, 4,......................................$40.00-50.00

Page 63, Donatello
Row 1:
    1. Flower Pot and Saucer $125.00-150.00
    2. Compote, 4"...................................$75.00-100.00
    3. Bowl, 3½".....................................$100.00-150.00
    4. Bowl, 3"...$55.00-85.00
Row 2:
    1. Double Bud Vase, 5".........................$50.00-75.00
    2. Compote, 5"..................................$100.00-125.00
    3. Vase, 6"...$45.00-60.00
    4. Candlestick, 8", pr $125.00-175.00
    5. Vase, 8"...$95.00-120.00
Row 3:
    1. Pitcher, 6½"...................................$200.00-250.00
    2. Vase, 10"....................................$250.00-300.00
    3. Wall Pocket, 10"............................$150.00-200.00
    4. Jardiniere, 6"................................$75.00-100.00
Row 4:
    1. Basket,15"...................................$300.00-400.00
    2. Jardiniere, 8½"..............................$100.00-150.00
    3. Frog $10.00-20.00
    4. Jardiniere, 7"................................$75.00-125.00

Page 65, Juvenille
Row 1:
    1. Mug, 3"..$75.00-100.00
    2. Bowl, 5½" (under mug) $80.00-110.00
    3. Two-handled Mug, 3" $90.00-120.00
    4. Baby's Plate, 6½" $100.00-150.00
    5. Oatmeal Bowl, 5½" $100.00-150.00
    6. Footed Egg Cup, 3" $200.00-250.00
    7. Mug, 3½" $75.00-125.00
Row 2:
    1. Plate, 7" $100.00-125.00
    2. Mug, 3" $75.00-95.00
    3. Plate, 8" $100.00-135.00
    4. Two-handled Mug, 3" $90.00-120.00
    5. Rolled-edge Plate, 8" $125.00-175.00
Row 3:
    1. Rolled-edge Plate, 8" $125.00-200.00
    2. Creamer, 3½" $100.00-125.00
    3. Rolled-edge Plate, 8" $120.00-200.00
    4. Creamer, 3½" $85.00-120.00
    5. Rolled-edge Plate, 8" $125.00-200.00
Bottom
    1. Milk Pitcher $75.00-100.00
    2. Side-pour Creamer $65.00-90.00
    3. Chamber $350.00-500.00
    4. Pitcher..$80.00-120.00
    5. Milk Pitcher $60.00-90.00

Page 67, Rozane, 1917
Row 1:
    1. Basket, 6" $100.00-125.00
    2. Candlestick, 6", pr. $75.00-100.00
    3. Spittoon, 5" $150.00-200.00
    4. Compote, 5" $70.00-90.00
Row 2:
    1. Basket, 8" $125.00-150.00
    2. Basket, 11" $125.00-175.00
    3. Champagne Bucket $250.00-350.00
    4. Vase, 7" $75.00-110.00

Velmoss Scroll
    Jardiniere and Pedestal, 30"...................$800.00-1,100.00
Row 1:
    1. Candlestick, 8" pr. $150.00-200.00
    2. Bowl, 2½"x9"..$55.00-75.00
    3. Candlestick, 9" pr. $150.00-200.00
Row 2:
    1. Vase, 6" $90.00-110.00
    2. Compote, 9", dia. $110.00-135.00
    3. Candlestick, 11", pr $175.00-250.00

Page 69, Rosecraft
    1. Vase, 8" $100.00-125.00
    2. Vase, 6" $75.00-95.00
    3. Bowl, 2½" $50.00-75.00
    4. Frog $10.00-15.00

Florane
    1. Bowl, 8" $50.00-60.00
    2. Vase, 6" $50.00-60.00
    3. Bud Vases, 8", each................................$50.00-70.00
    4. Urn Vase, 3½" $50.00-60.00
Rosecraft Black
    Vase, 10"...$125.00-175.00

Persian
    1. Sugar and Creamer $140.00-170.00
    2. Jardiniere $200.00-300.00
    3. Bowl, 3½" $100.00-150.00

Page 71, Savona
    Vase, 10"..$150.00-200.00

Normandy
    Jardiniere, 7" $175.00-225.00

Victorian Art Pottery
    1. Covered Jar, 8" $500.00-700.00
    2. Jardiniere, 10" $600.00-800.00

Corinthian
Row 1:
    1. Vase, 6" $70.00-80.00
    2. Compote, 10" dia. $90.00-110.00
    3. Ashtray, 2" $70.00-80.00
    4. Double Bud Vase, 7" $75.00-100.00
Row 2:
    1. Candlestick, 8", ea. $60.00-85.00
    2. Vase, 8" $85.00-120.00
    3. Vase, 10½" $125.00-150.00
    4. Vase, 8" $80.00-120.00
    5. Candlestick, 10", ea. $70.00-85.00

Page 73, Dogwood I
Row 1:
    2. Wall Pocket $200.00-275.00
    3. Vase, 6" $100.00-125.00

Dogwood II
Row 1:
    1. Basket, 6" $110.00-150.00
    4. Bowl, 2" $50.00-75.00
Row 2:
    1. Basket, 8" $115.00-160.00
    2. Planter, 6" $95.00-120.00
    3. Double Wall Pocket.................................$200.00-300.00
    4. Bud Vase, 8" $75.00-110.00
Row 3:
    1. Vase, 8" $100.00-150.00
    2. Bud Vase, 9" $60.00-85.00
    3. Vase, 9" $110.00-140.00
    4. Vase, 12" $200.00-350.00
    5. Jardiniere, 8" $200.00-250.00

Page 75, Rosecraft Vintage
Row 1:
    1. Vase, 5" $100.00-125.00
    2. Bowl, 5" $100.00-120.00
    3. Vase, 8" $150.00-200.00
    4. Candlestick, 8" pr $200.00-250.00
    5. Bowl, 6" $75.00-100.00
Row 2:
    1. Jardiniere, 9" $300.00-400.00
    2. Bowl, 3½" $50.00-75.00
    3. Urn Vase, 10" $275.00-350.00
    4. Jardiniere, 8" $300.00-350.00

Rosecraft Hexagon
    1. Vase, 6" $150.00-200.00
    2. Bowl, Vase, 4" $175.00-225.00
    3. Same as #1

Page 77, Panel
Row 1:
    1. Double Bud Vase $100.00-150.00
    2. Fan Vase, 6" $275.00-325.00
    3. Fan Vase, 8" $300.00-375.00
    4. Candleholder, 2", pr. $50.00-70.00
    5. Pillow Vase, 6" $95.00-110.00

Row 2:
  1. Candlestick, 8", pr. $200.00-275.00
  2. Urn Vase, 8" $200.00-250.00
  3. Vase, 9" $225.00-275.00
  4. Vase, 8" $150.00-200.00

La Rose
Row 1:
  1. Bowl, 6" $50.00-75.00
  2. Bowl, 9" $75.00-110.00
  3. Candleholders, 4", pr. $125.00-200.00
Row 2:
  1. Double Bud Vase $75.00-100.00
  2. Vase, 10" $150.00-225.00

Page 79, Dahlrose
Row 1:
  1. Triple Bud Vase, 6" $100.00-135.00
  2. Square Vase, 6" $125.00-175.00
  3. Bowl, 10" $150.00-200.00
  4. Double Bud Vase $75.00-125.00
Row 2:
  1. Vase, 8" $175.00-250.00
  2. Square Vase, 10" $150.00-200.00
  3. Vase, 10" $200.00-250.00
  4. Vase, 10" $250.00-300.00
  5. Bud Vase, 8" $150.00-200.00

Tuscany
Row 1:
  1. Candleholders, 4", pr. $50.00-60.00
  2. Flower Arranger Vase, 5" $50.00-60.00
  3. Candleholders, 3", pr. $50.00-75.00
Row 2:
  1. Vase, 8" $50.00-80.00
  2. Console Bowl, 11" $75.00-95.00
  3. Vase, 8" $100.00-125.00

Page 81, Florentine
  1. Double Bud Vase, 6" $90.00-110.00
  2. Basket, 8"....................................$150.00-200.00
  3. Footed Compote, 10"...........................$90.00-120.00
  4. Vase, 9" $80.00-110.00
  5. Lamp $225.00-325.00
  6. Compote, 5" $50.00-75.00
  7. Wall Pocket, 7" $125.00-175.00
  8. Vase, 8½" $100.00-135.00
  9. Wall Pocket, 9½" $175.00-225.00
  10. Vase, 6½" $70.00-90.00
  11. Bowl, 9" $50.00-60.00

Lustre
  1. Candleholder, 8", pr. $50.00-60.00
  2. Candleholder, 10", pr. $65.00-85.00
  3. Vase, 10" $65.00-75.00
  4. Same as #2
  5. Candleholder, 6", pr. $45.00-55.00

Carnelian II
  1. Vase, 6½" $250.00-400.00

Imperial II
  2. Wall Pocket....................................$350.00-400.00

Page 83, Futura
Top:
  1. Vase, 8" $400.00-450.00
  2. Vase, 8" $800.00-1,100.00
  3. Vase, 6" $400.00-500.00

Row 1:
  1. Bud Vase, 6" $175.00-225.00
  2. Candleholder, 4", pr $150.00-200.00
  3. Planter, 7" $150.00-175.00
  4. Same as #2
  5. Vase, 6" $200.00-250.00
Row 2:
  1. Vase, 8" $275.00-325.00
  2. Bud Vase, 10" $350.00-400.00
  3. Urn, 10" $800.00-1,000.00
  4. Vase, Sea Gulls, 10" $800.00-1,100.00
  5. Vase, 8" $500.00-600.00

Cremona
  Vase, 10" $100.00-125.00
Row 1:
  1. Candleholder, 4", pr. $50.00-60.00
  2. Vase, 7" $50.00-70.00
Row 2:
  1. Vase, 10½" $100.00-125.00
  2. Frog $15.00-20.00
  3. Bowl, 9" $60.00-80.00
  4. Vase, 8" $60.00-70.00

Page 85, Earlam
Row 1:
  1. Candleholder, 6", pr. $100.00-150.00
  2. Wall Pot (questionable origin) Burley-Winters
Row 2:
  1. Urn, 6" (Artcraft Glaze) $100.00-150.00
  2. Vase, 6" $125.00-175.00

Ixia
Row 1:
  1. Basket, 10", No. 346 ....$100.00-150.00
  2. Vase, 6", No. 853 ....$50.00-70.00
Row 2:
  1. Bowl, 4", No. 326 ....$50.00-75.00
  2. Bowl, 6", No. 387 ....$60.00-85.00

Clemana
  Vase, 7"..$100.00-150.00
  Candleholders. 4½", pr. $110.00-160.00

Sunflower
Row 1:
  1. Urn, 5½" $300.00-350.00
  2. Vase, 8" $400.00-500.00
  3. Vase, 7" $250.00-350.00
  4. Vase, 6" $200.00-225.00
Row 2:
  1. Vase, 10" $475.00-575.00
  2. Jardiniere, 9" $450.00-550.00
  3. Vase, 8" $400.00-500.00

Page 87, Thornapple
Row 1:
  1. Cornucopia Vase, 6" $50.00-75.00
  2. Planter, 5", No. 262 ....$60.00-80.00
  3. Vase, 6", No. 812 ....$50.00-75.00
Row 2:
  1. Candleholders, 2½", pr. $75.00-90.00
  2. Candleholder, 5½", pr. $110.00-125.00
Row 3:
  1. Vase, 4", No. 308 ....$60.00-85.00
  2. Basket, 10", No. 342 ....$200.00-250.00

Iris
Row 1:
  1. Bowl, Vase, 4", No. 2117 ....$50.00-60.00
  2. Wall Shelf, 8" $200.00-275.00
  3. Bowl, 5", No. 359 ....$125.00-150.00

Row 2:
    1. Vase, 4", No. 914 ....$50.00-60.00
    2. Planter, 14", No. 364 ....$175.00-250.00
    3. Candleholder, 4", No. 1135, pr. $85.00-110.00
Row 3:
    1. Ewer, 10", No. 926 ....$200.00-275.00
    2. Basket, 8", No. 354 ....$200.00-250.00

Poppy
Row 1:
    1. Wall Pocket, Candleholder, 9", No. 1281 ....$275.00-350.00
    2. Vase, 6½" $75.00-110.00
Row 2:
    1. Ewer, 10", No.876 ....$150.00-200.00
    2. Basket, 10", No. 347 ....$150.00-200.00

Moss
Row 1:
    Candleholders, 4½", No. 1107 ....$90.00-110.00
Row 2:
    1. Vase, 6", No 744* $100.00-125.00
    2. Urn, 8", No. 774 ....$150.00-175.00
        (*Identical numbers were found on these two items)
Row 3:
    Console Bowl, 13" $175.00-225.00

Page 89, Ferella
Top:
    1. Vase, 4" $175.00-225.00
    2. Vase, 9" $350.00-450.00
    3. Bowl, 12" $375.00-475.00
    4. Vase, 6" $200.00-250.00
    5. Vase, 9" $300.00-400.00

Falline
Center:
    1. Vase, 6" $225.00-275.00
    2. Urn Vase, 8" $250.00-300.00
    3. Lamp $500.00-600.00
    4. Vase, 7" $250.00-300.00
    5. Vase, 6" $225.00-250.00

Tourmaline
Bottom:
    Ginger Jar $150.00-175.00
Row 1:
    1. Bowl Vase, 5" $50.00-60.00
    2. Vase, 8" $60.00-70.00
    3. Frog $10.00-15.00
Row 2:
    1. Vase, 6" $60.00-75.00
    2. Planter, 12½" $100.00-125.00
    3. Vase, 6" $60.00-75.00

Page 91, Monticello
Row 1:
    1. Vase, 4" $75.00-100.00
    2. Basket, 6½" $200.00-225.00
    3. Vase, 4" $75.00-100.00
Row 2:
    1. Vase, 6" $150.00-200.00
    2. Vase, 7" $175.00-225.00
Row 3:
    1. Vase, 7" $175.00-225.00
    2. Urn, 9" $225.00-275.00

Windsor
Row 1:
    1. Candlestick, 4½", pr. $175.00-225.00
    2. Vase, 5" $125.00-150.00

Row 2:
    1. Vase, 5" $125.00-150.00
    2. Console with Frog $150.00-200.00
Row 3:
    1. Vase, 7" $275.00-350.00
    2. Vase, 9" $350.00-400.00

Cosmos
Row 1:
    1. Vase, No. 954 ....$50.00-60.00
    2. Bowl, 6", No. 376 ....$75.00-100.00
    3. Vase, 3" $50.00-60.00
Row 2:
    1. Basket, 12" $300.00-400.00
    2. Candleholder, 2½", pr. $90.00-110.00
    3. Ewer, 15", No. 951 ....$300.00-400.00
        Window Box – Blue $250.00-300.00

Jonquil
Row 1:
    1. Bowl, 4" $60.00-75.00
    2. Basket, 9" $175.00-225.00
    3. Bud Vase, 7" $65.00-90.00
    4. Bowl, 4" $60.00-75.00
Row 2:
    1. Vase, 8" $150.00-200.00
    2. Basket, 10" $200.00-275.00
    3. Bowl, 5½" $100.00-140.00

Page 93, Blackberry
Row 1:
    1. Jug, 5" $225.00-275.00
    2. Vase, 4" $200.00-250.00
    3. Vase, 6" $275.00-350.00
    4. Wall Pocket $550.00-750.00
    5. Bowl, 8" $200.00-250.00
Row 2:
    1. Urn Vase, 6" $250.00-300.00
    2. Jardiniere, 6" $275.00-325.00
    3. Vase, 6" $250.00-300.00
    4. Vase, 5" $225.00-275.00
Row 3:
    1. Candleholder, 4½", pr. $300.00-400.00
    2. Console Bowl, 13" $250.00-350.00
    3. Vase, 4" $200.00-250.00
Row 4:
    1. Vase, 8" $300.00-375.00
    2. Vase, 10" $400.00-475.00
    3. Vase, 12½" $750.00-950.00
    4. Vase, 8" $300.00-375.00

Page 95, Cherry Blossom
Row 1:
    1. Candleholder, 4", pr. $250.00-300.00
    2. Bowl, 6" $275.00-325.00
    3. Bowl, 5" $200.00-250.00
Row 2:
    1. Vase, 5" $200.00-250.00
    2. Vase, 7½" $225.00-275.00
    3. Vase, 10" $325.00-400.00
    4. Jug Vase, 7" $225.00-275.00
Row 3:
    1. Vase, 5" $175.00-225.00
    2. Vase, 7" $200.00-250.00
    3. Vase, 8" $225.00-275.00
    4. Jug Vase, 7" $225.00-275.00
    5. Jug Vase, 4" $150.00-200.00

Row 4:
    1. Lamp Base $450.00-575.00
    2. Jardiniere, 10" $600.00-800.00
    3. Urn Vase, 8" $350.00-450.00

Page 97, Baneda
Row 1:
    1. Vase, 5½" $175.00-225.00
    2. Candleholder, 4½", pr. $225.00-275.00
    3. Console, 13" $225.00-275.00
    4. Vase, 6" $200.00-250.00
Row 2:
    1. Vase, 8" $250.00-300.00
    2. Jardiniere, 9½" $450.00-550.00
    3. Vase, 8" $250.00-300.00

Wisteria
Row 1:
    1. Console Bowl, 12" $225.00-275.00
    2. Vase, 7" $300.00-400.00
    3. Vase, 6" $200.00-250.00
    4. Bowl, 4" $200.00-250.00
Row 2:
    1. Vase, 8" $325.00-425.00
    2. Vase, 9" $350.00-450.00
    3. Vase, 10" $425.00-475.00
    4. Urn, 7½" $300.00-400.00

Page 99, Laurel
Row 1:
    1. Bowl, 7" $100.00-125.00
    2. Vase, 7" $125.00-175.00
    3. Vase, 6½" $125.00-150.00
    4. Vase, 6" $100.00-150.00
Row 2:
    1. Vase, 8" $150.00-200.00
    2. Vase, 9" $150.00-225.00
    3. Vase, 8½" $175.00-250.00
    4. Vase, 6" $125.00-150.00

Luffa
Bottom:
    1. Bowl, 4" $60.00-80.00
    2. Vase, 7" $125.00-175.00
    3. Vase, 13" $300.00-400.00
    4. Vase, 7" $125.00-175.00
    5. Vase, 6" $125.00-150.00

Page 101, Topeo
Plate 98
    Vase, 9½" $200.00-250.00
Plate 99
    1. Vase, 7" $150.00-200.00
    2. Vase, 9" $175.00-225.00
Row 1:
    Bowl, 2½" $100.00-150.00
Row 2:
    1. Urn, 6" $150.00-175.00
    2. Vase, 6½" $150.00-175.00

Primrose
Bottom:
    1. Vase, 8" $125.00-175.00
    2. Bowl, 4" $75.00-100.00
    3. Vase, 8", No 765 ....$150.00-200.00

Page 103, Pinecone
Row 1:
    1. Triple Candleholder, 5½", No. 1106 ....$200.00-250.00
    2. Bowl, 3", No. 632 ....$60.00-75.00
    3. Planter, 8", No. 468 ....$125.00-150.00
    4. Planter, 6", No. 456 ....$100.00-135.00
    5. Basket, 6", No. 408 ....$135.00-185.00
Row 2:
    1. Fan Vase, 6", No. 472 ....$100.00-150.00
    2. Console Bowl, 15", No. 323 ....$225.00-325.00
    3. Cornucopia, 8", No. 128 ....$100.00-125.00

Row 3:
    1. Ice Lip Pitcher, 8" $300.00-400.00
    2. Cornucopia, 6", No. 126 ....$75.00-100.00
    3. Boat-basket, 10", No. 410 ....$250.00-300.00
    4. Pitcher, 9", No. 415 ....$325.00-375.00
Row 4:
    1. Vase, 10", No. 109 ....$225.00-325.00
    2. Basket, 9", No. 339 ....$550.00-650.00
    3. Vase, 7", No. 478 ....$125.00-150.00
    4. Basket 10", No. 338 ....$350.00-400.00

Page 105, Orian
Top:
    1. Vase, 7" $110.00-135.00
    2. Vase, 8" $125.00-150.00
    3. Vase, 12" $150.00-200.00
    4. Bowl, 6" $100.00-125.00

Russco
Center:
    1. Vase, 14½", Matt $125.00-175.00
    2. Vase, 6½" $60.00-85.00
    3. Bud Vase, 8", Crystals $90.00-110.00
    4. Vase, 6" $125.00-175.00

Velmoss II
    1. Vase, 7" $50.00-75.00
    2. Double Bud, 8" $65.00-85.00
    3. Vase, 6" $60.00-75.00
    4. Double Cornucopia, 8½" $85.00-115.00

Page 107, Morning Glory
Row 1:
    1. Bowl Vase, 4" $175.00-225.00
    2. Urn Vase, 6" $225.00-275.00
    3. Vase, 7" $200.00-250.00
    4. Vase, 6" $200.00-250.00
Row 2:
    1. Vase, 8" $250.00-300.00
    2. Vase, 12" $450.00-650.00
    3. Vase, 10" $350.00-450.00

Teasel
Row 1
    1. Vase, 5" $50.00-60.00
    2. Vase, 6", No. 348 ....$55.00-75.00
    3. Vase, 6", No. 882 ....$55.00-75.00
    4. Bowl, 4", No. 342 ....$50.00-60.00
Row 2:
    1. Basket, 10", No. 349 ....$175.00-250.00
    2. Ewer, 18", No. 890 ....$225.00-275.00
    3. Basket, 10" $175.00-250.00

Dawn
Bottom, left:
    1. Vase, 6", No. 827 ....$90.00-115.00
    2. Vase, 8", No. 828 ....$100.00-125.00
    3. Vase, 6", No. 826 ....$90.00-110.00

Moderne
Bottom, right:
    1. Lamp, 9", No 799 ....$250.00-400.00
    2. Vase, 7", No. 794 ....$60.00-90.00

Page 109, Fuchsia
Row 1:
    Pitcher, 8", No. 1322 ....$250.00-300.00
Row 2:
    1. Bowl, 4", No. 346 ....$65.00-90.00
    2. Vase, 3", No. 645 ....$50.00-80.00

Row 3:
1. Vase, 7", No. 895 ....$150.00-200.00
2. Vase, 12", No. 903 ....$250.00-350.00
3. Basket and Frog, 8" $250.00-325.00

Ivory ll
Top:
1. Vase, 10" $65.00-90.00
2. Vase, 6" $60.00-80.00
Row 1:
Bowl, 6", No. 259 ....$50.00-70.00
Row 2:
1. Candelabra, 5½", pr. $100.00-150.00
2. Bowl, 6", No. 550 ....$30.00-40.00

Bleeding Heart
Row 1:
1. Vase, 4", No. 138 ....$50.00-60.00
2. Wall Pocket, 8", No. 1287 ....$250.00-300.00
3. Pitcher, No. 1323 ....$150.00-200.00
4. Ewer, 6", No. 963 ....$90.00-115.00
Row 2:
1. Basket, 10", No. 360 ....$150.00-200.00
2. Basket, 12", No. 361 ....$175.00-225.00
3. Ewer, 10", No. 972 ....$125.00-175.00

Page 111, Rozane Pattern
Top, left:
1. Bud Vase, 6", No. 2 ....$50.00-60.00
2. Planter, 14", No. 397 ....$50.00-70.00
3. Vase, 6", No. 398 ....$60.00-80.00

Gardenia
Top, right:
Row 1:
Bowl, 4", No. 600 ....$30.00-40.00
Row 2:
1. Cornucopia, 6", No. 621 ....$35.00-40.00
2. Basket, 8", No. 608 ....$100.00-125.00
3. Ewer, 6", No. 616 ....$50.00-60.00
Row 3:
1. Ewer, 10", No. 617 ....$90.00-100.00
2. Basket, 10", No. 609 ....$100.00-135.00
3. Double Cornucopia, 8", No. 622 ....$50.00-60.00

Bittersweet
Row 1:
1. Double Bud Vase, 6", No. 873 ....$50.00-60.00
2. Basket, 10", No. 810 ....$100.00-150.00
3. Vase, 5", No. 972 ....$45.00-55.00
Row 2:
1. Planter, 8", No. 868 ....$40.00-50.00
2. Tea Set, No. 871 ....$225.00-300.00
Row 3:
1. Basket, 6", No. 808 ....$50.00-75.00
2. Basket, 8", No. 809 ....$75.00-100.00
3. Vase, 8", No. 883 ....$80.00-110.00
4. Cornucopia, 8", No. 882 ....$45.00-55.00
5. Ewer, 8", No. 816 ....$60.00-75.00

Page 113, White Rose
Row 1:
1. Frog, No. 41 ....$30.00-50.00
2. Cornucopia, 6", No. 143 ....$40.00-55.00

3. Bowl, 4", No. 387 ....$50.00-75.00
4. Bowl, 3", No 653 ....$40.00-50.00
Row 2:
1. Cornucopia, 8", No. 144 ....$50.00-65.00
2. Basket, 10", No. 363 ....$150.00-225.00
3. Bowl, 4", No. 653 ....$50.00-75.00
4. Ewer, 10", No. 990 ....$175.00-225.00

Row 3:
1. Double Cornucopia, 8", No. 145 ....$50.00-65.00
2. Tea Set, No. 1 ....$250.00-350.00
3. Urn Vase, 8", No. 147 ....$100.00-150.00
Row 4:
1. Basket, 12", No. 364 ....$125.00-150.00
2. Ewer, 15", No. 993 ....$200.00-275.00
3. Ewer, 6", No 981 ....$60.00-80.00
4. Pitcher, No. 1324 ....$100.00-140.00

Page 115, Water Lily
Row 1:
1. Bowl, 3", No. 663 ....$40.00-50.00
2. Ewer, 6", No. 10 ....$50.00-60.00
3. Vase, 6", No. 73 ....$50.00-60.00
4. Cornucopia, 6", No. 177 ....$45.00-55.00
Row 2:
1. Ewer, 10", No. 11 ....$125.00-175.00
2. Cookie jar, 10", No. 1 ....$350.00-450.00
3. Basket, 10", No. 381 ....$100.00-125.00
4. Vase, 10", No. 81 ....$125.00-175.00
Row 3:
1. Vase, 7", No. 75 ....$75.00-100.00
2. Cornucopia, 8", No. 178 ....$60.00-80.00
3. Vase, 6", No. 72 ....$45.00-55.00
4. Basket, 8", No. 380 ....$100.00-150.00
Row 4:
1. Vase, 12", No. 81 ....$125.00-175.00
2. Basket, 12", No. 382 ....$150.00-225.00
3. Ewer, 15", No. 12 ....$250.00-300.00

Page 117, Zephyr Lily
Row 1:
1. Bowl, 4", No. 671 ....$50.00-65.00
2. Console Boat, 10", No. 475 ....$90.00-115.00
3. Bowl, 8", No. 474 ....$90.00-110.00
Row 2:
1. Basket, 7", No. 393 ....$90.00-110.00
2. Cookie Jar, 10", No. 5 ....$350.00-450.00
3. Ashtray $50.00-60.00
4. Vase, 10", No. 138 ....$125.00-175.00
Row 3:
1. Basket, 8", No. 394 ....$90.00-120.00
2. Tea Set, No. 7 ....$250.00-350.00
3. Cornucopia, 6", No. 203 ....$45.00-55.00
Row 4:
1. Basket, 10", No. 395 ....$125.00-175.00
2. Vase, 7", No. 131 ....$75.00-100.00
3. Ewer, 15", No. 24 ....$225.00-275.00
4. Ewer, 10", No. 23 ....$125.00-175.00
5. Vase, 10", No. 137 ....$125.00-150.00

Page 119, Peony
Row 1:
1. Bowl, 4", No. 427 ....$40.00-50.00
2. Vase, 6", No. 168 ....$45.00-55.00
3. Bowl, 4", No. 427 ....$50.00-60.00
Row 2:
1. Double Cornucopia, No. 172 ....$55.00-75.00
2. Basket, 10", No. 378 ....$150.00-200.00
3. Basket, 7", No. 376 ....$120.00-160.00
Row 3:
1. Ewer, 6", No. 7 ....$45.00-55.00
2. Tea Set, No. 3 ....$225.00-325.00
3. Bowl, 4", No. 661 ....$40.00-50.00
Row 4:
1. Vase, 4", No. 57 ....$30.00-35.00
2. Ewer, 10", No. 8 ....$125.00-150.00
3. Same as #2
4. Wall Pocket, 8", No. 1293 ....$150.00-225.00

Page 121, Magnolia
Row 1:
    1. Planter, 8", No. 389 ....$100.00-125.00
    2. Double Bud Vase, No. 186.....................$65.00-90.00
    3. Vase, 4", No. 86 ....$40.00-50.00
    4. Bowl, 3", No. 665 ....$35.00-45.00
Row 2:
    1. Ewer, 6", No. 13 ....$60.00-90.00
    2. Mug, 3", No. 3..$90.00-120.00
    3. Cider Pitcher, 7", No. 132 ....$225.00-325.00
    4. Basket, 8", No. 384 ....$125.00-175.00
Row 3:
    1. Basket, 7", No. 384 ....$100.00-125.00
    2. Tea Set, No. 4 ....$250.00-350.00
Row 4:
    1. Basket, 10", No. 385 ....$125.00-175.00
    2. Ewer, 15", No. 15 ....$250.00-300.00
    3. Cookie Jar, 10", No. 2 ....$350.00-450.00

Page 123, Columbine
Row 1:
    1. Ewer, 7", No. 18 ....$60.00-75.00
    2. Bowl, 6", No. 401 ....$35.00-40.00
    3. Basket, 7", No. 365 ....$125.00-150.00
    4. Ewer, 7", No. 18 ....$60.00-75.00
Row 2:
    1. Basket, 10", No. 367 ....$100.00-150.00
    2. Bowl, 3", No. 655 ....$30.00-35.00
    3. Basket, 12", No. 368 ....$175.00-250.00
    4. Vase, 8", No. 20 ....$70.00-90.00

Foxglove
Row 1:
    1. Vase, 4", No. 42 ....$25.00-35.00
    2. Vase, 3", No. 659 ....$25.00-30.00
    3. Basket, 8", No. 373 ....$125.00-175.00
    4. Conch Shell, 6", No. 426 ....$60.00-90.00
    5. Double Bud Vase, 4½", No. 160 ....$75.00-100.00
Row 2:
    1. Ewer, 6½", No. 4 ....$65.00-90.00
    2. Cornucopia, 8", No. 164.........................$50.00-70.00
    3. Candleholder, 4½", No. 1150, pr. $100.00-150.00
    4. Ewer, 15", No. 6 ....$200.00-250.00
    5. Ewer, 10", No. 5 ....$175.00-225.00

Page 125, Freesia
Row 1:
    1. Ewer, 6", No. 19 ....$60.00-90.00
    2. Flower Pot, 5", No. 670 ....$75.00-110.00
    3. Bookends, pr., No. 15 ....$150.00-200.00
Row 2:
    1. Basket, 8", No. 391 ....$125.00-140.00
    2. Pitcher, 10", No. 20 ....$175.00-225.00
    3. Basket, 10", No. 392 ....$175.00-225.00
    4. Cornucopia, 8", No. 198.........................$50.00-60.00
Row 3:
    1. Vase, 8", No. 122 ....$75.00-100.00
    2. Tea Set, No 6 ....$250.00-350.00
    3. Vase, 7", No. 120 ....$75.00-90.00
Row 4:
    1. Cookie Jar, 10", No. 4 ....$350.00-450.00
    2. Ewer, 15", No. 21 ....$300.00-325.00
    3. Urn, 8", No. 196 ....$125.00-150.00
    4. Candleholder, 4½", No. 1161 ....$70.00-90.00
    5. Bud Vase, 7", No. 195 ....$65.00-90.00

Page 127, Clematis
Row 1:
    1. Bowl, 4", No. 445 ....$30.00-40.00
    2. Double Bud Vase, 5", No. 194 ....$40.00-50.00
    3. Cornucopia, 6", No. 140.........................$30.00-40.00
    4. Candleholder, 4½", No. 11, pr $70.00-90.00

Row 2:
    1. Basket, 8", No. 388 ....$100.00-125.00
    2. Bud Vase, 7", No. 187 ....$50.00-70.00
    3. Ewer, 10", No. 17 ....$100.00-135.00
    4. Basket, 7", No. 387 ....$100.00-130.00
    5. Ewer, 6", No. 16 ....$60.00-80.00
Row 3:
    1. Vase, 8", No. 108 ....$50.00-70.00
    2. Tea Set, No. 5 ....$250.00-350.00
    3. Vase, 6", No. 188 ....$50.00-60.00
Row 4:
    1. Cookie Jar, 10", No. 3 ....$300.00-400.00
    2. Wall Pocket, 8", No. 1295 ....$110.00-160.00
    3. Ewer, 15", No. 18 ....$200.00-250.00
    4. Basket, 10", No. 389 ....$120.00-165.00

Page 129, Apple Blossom
Row 1:
    1. Cornucopia, 6", No. 381 ....$40.00-50.00
    2. Hanging Basket $125.00-175.00
    3. Vase, 6", No. 381 ....$75.00-90.00
Row 2:
    1. Tea Set, No. 371 ....$250.00-350.00
    2. Basket, 8", No. 309 ....$125.00-175.00
Row 3:
    1. Ewer, 8", No. 316 ....$90.00-115.00
    2. Vase, 7", No. 382 ....$60.00-85.00
    3. Basket, 10", No. 310 ....$150.00-225.00
    4. Bud Vase, 7", No. 379...........................$60.00-90.00
Row 4.
    1. Vase, 9", No. 387 ....$100.00-150.00
    2. Ewer, 15, No. 318 ....$300.00-400.00
    3. Basket, 12", No. 311 ....$150.00-175.00

Page 131, Bushberry
Row 1:
    1. Bowl, 4", No. 411 ....$50.00-60.00
    2. Basket, 6½", No. 369 ....$75.00-95.00
    3. Cornucopia, 6", No. 153.........................$50.00-60.00
    4. Vase, 6", No. 29 ....$55.00-75.00
    5. Bowl, 3", No. 657 ....$40.00-50.00
Row 2:
    1. Ewer, 6", No 1 ....$60.00-75.00
    2. Cornucopia, No.3.....................................$75.00-110.00
    3. Wall Pocket, 8", No. 1291 ....$300.00-350.00
    4. Basket, 8", No. 370 ....$110.00-140.00
Row 3:
    Tea Set, No. 2 ....$250.00-350.00
Row 4:
    1. Ewer, 10", No. 2 ....$125.00-175.00
    2. Basket, 12", No. 372 ....$225.00-275.00
    3. Cornucopia, 8", No. 154.........................$50.00-75.00

Page 133, Snowberry
Row 1:
    1. Ashtray...$45.00-50.00
    2. Console Bowl, 10", No. 1BL1.................$75.00-100.00
    3. Ewer, 6", No. 1TK $60.00-90.00
Row 2:
    1. Basket, 7", No. 1BK $75.00-100.00
    2. Cornucopia, 6", No 1CC $35.00-45.00
    3. Basket, 8", No. 1BK $100.00-125.00
    4. Bowl, 5", No. 1RB $60.00-80.00
Row 3:
    1. Ewer, 6", No. 1TK $45.00-60.00
    2. Tea Set, No. 1TP, No. 1S, No. 1C $250.00-350.00
    3. Bud Vase, 7", No. 1BV $40.00-60.00
Row 4:
    1. Basket, 8", No. 1BK $100.00-135.00
    2. Ewer, 10", No. 1TK..................................$80.00-110.00

3. Candleholders, No. 1CS-1, pr. $50.00-60.00
4. Basket, 10", No. 1BK $125.00-175.00

Page 135, Mock Orange
Row 1:
    1. Bowl, 4", No. 900 ....$25.00-35.00
    2. Basket, 6", No. 908 ....$75.00-100.00
    3. Ewer, 6", No. 916 ....$50.00-60.00
Row 2:
    1. Tall Planter $45.00-55.00
Row 3:
    1. Basket, 8", No. 909 ....$75.00-110.00

Ming Tree
Row 1:
    1. Pr. Candleholders, No. 551 ....$55.00-75.00
    2. Basket, 8", No. 508 ....$100.00-125.00
Row 2:
    1. Console Bowl, 10", No. 528 ....$75.00-110.00
Row 3:
    1. Vase, 8", No. 582 ....$60.00-90.00
    2. Ewer, 10", No. 516 ....$80.00-110.00
    3. Vase, 6", No. 581 ....$50.00-60.00

Mayfair
Center:
    1. Bowl, 4", No. 1110 ....$20.00-25.00
    2. Pitcher, 8", No. 1105 ....$60.00-70.00
    3. Tankard, 12", No. 1107 ....$65.00-75.00
    4. Planter, 8", No. 113 ....$25.00-30.00

Burmese
    1. Candleholder/Bookends, pr.
       White, No. 80-B $200.00-275.00
       Black, No. 70-B $300.00-350.00
    2. Candlestick, No. 75-B, pr. $90.00-110.00

Royal Capri
    Bowl, 7" $165.00-195.00

Page 137, Lotus
    1. Candleholders, 2½", No., L5, pr. $80.00-115.00
    2. Vase, 10", No. L3 ....$150.00-200.00
Pasadena
    1. Occasional piece, 7", No. 526.................................$25.00-30.00
    2. Flower Pot, 4", No. L36 ....$35.00-40.00
    3. Bowl, 3", No. L24 ....$35.00-40.00
        (#1 not Pasadena; from a late unidentified line)

Unnamed Line
Row 1:
    1. Vase, 9", No. 582 ....$40.00-50.00
    2. Occasional Piece, 15", No. 532 ....$35.00-40.00
    3. Boat Dish, 7", No. 555 ....$30.00-35.00
Row 2:
    1. Conch Shell, 7½", No. 563 ....$40.00-45.00
    2. Shell $40.00-45.00
    3. Bowl, 9", No. 529 ....$20.00-25.00
    4. Teapot, No. 14-P $45.00-50.00
    (The last two items in Row 1 and the two in the center of Row 2 have
    been identified as Capri; the Conch shell is from the Ming Tree line.)

Page 137, Late Line, Florane (see Vol. ll)
    1. Vase, 6", No. 80 ....$40.00-50.00
    2. Vase, 7", No. 81 ....$50.00-60.00
    3. Vase, 9", No. 82 ....$60.00-75.00
    4. Bowl, No. 61 ....$40.00-50.00

Page 139, Silhouette
Row 1:
    1. Pr. Candleholder, 3", No. 751 ....$45.00-55.00
    2. Planter, 14", No. 731 ....$50.00-60.00
Row 2:
    1. Planter Vase, 5", No. 756 ....$30.00-40.00
    2. Ewer, 6", No. 716 ....$50.00-65.00
    3. Ewer, 10", No. 717 ....$75.00-90.00
    4. Basket, 6", No. 708 ....$110.00-135.00
    5. Vase, 7", No. 782 ....$50.00-75.00
Row 3:
    1. Cornucopia, 8", No. 721 ....$30.00-35.00
    2. Fan Vase, 7", No. 783 ....$200.00-250.00
    3. Ashtray, No. 799 ....$30.00-35.00
    4. Basket, 8", No. 709 ....$75.00-110.00
Row 4:
    1. Basket, 10", No. 710 ....$135.00-185.00
    2. Cigarette Box $50.00-60.00
    3. Urn, 8", No. 763 ....$250.00-350.00
    4. Vase, 9", No. 785 ....$85.00-110.00
    5. Wall Pocket, 8", No. 766 ....$125.00-165.00

Page 141, Wincraft
Row 1:
    1. Planter Set, 6", No. 1050-51 ....$80.00-100.00
    2. Tea Set, No. 271 ....$125.00-175.00
Row 2:
    1. Basket, 12", No. 209 ....$100.00-125.00
    2. Candleholder, pr. No. 2CS $30.00-40.00
    3. Circle Vase, 8", No. 1053...$60.00-90.00
    4. Ewer, 8", No. 216 ....$40.00-50.00
    (The planter set in Row 1, and the Circle Vase in Row 2 have been
    identified as Artwood.)
Row 3:
    1. Planter, 10", No. 231 ....$60.00-80.00
    2. Cornucopia, 8", No. 222...$30.00-40.00
    3. Ewer, 6", No. 217 ....$40.00-50.00
    4. Basket, 8", No. 208 ....$70.00-90.00
Row 4:
    1. Vase, 8", No. 282 ....$50.00-60.00
    2. Vase, 10", No. 284 ....$70.00-95.00
    3. Vase, 10", No. 290 ....$250.00-300.00
    4. Vase, 10", No. 285 ....$100.00-125.00
    5. Vase, 6", No. 272 ....$45.00-55.00

Page 143, Elsie the Cow
    1. Mug, No. B1 ....$150.00-200.00
    2. Plate, 7½", No. B2 ....$200.00-300.00
    3. Bowl, No. B3 ....$150.00-200.00

Raymor
Top, right:
    1. Bean Pot, No. 195 ....$35.00-45.00
    2. Swinging Coffee Pot, No. 176..............................$175.00-225.00
    3. Bean Pot, No. 194 ....$25.00-30.00
Row 1:
    1. Hot Plate & Casserole, No. 84, No. 198 ....$50.00-60.00
    2. Hot Plate, No. 159 ....$15.00-20.00
    3. Cup & Saucer, No. 151 ....$25.00-30.00
Row 2:
    1. Tea Set, Sugar, No. 157, Cream, No. 158 ....$200.00-300.00
      (lid missing)
Row 3:
    1. Salad Plate, No. 154...$15.00-20.00
    2. Dinner Plate, No. 152 ....$20.00-30.00
    3. Luncheon Plate, No. 153 ....$15.00-20.00

Page 145, Jardinieres and Pedestals, Umbrella Stands
    Blackberry, Jard. and Ped 12" dia.........................$4,000.00-4,500.00
    Donatello, Jard. and Ped $450.00-550.00

Pine Cone, Jard. and Ped, 12" $3,500.00-4,500.00
Pine Cone, Jard. and Ped, 10" $2,500.00-3,500.00
Magnolia, Jard. and Ped,12".................................$600.00-700.00
Mostique, Umbrella Stand $250.00-300.00
Mostique, Jard. and Ped $400.00-500.00
Fuschia, Jard. and Ped $900.00-1,200.00
Freesia, Jard. and Ped $550.00-750.00

Page 147, Umbrella Stands and Sand Jars
Imperial I, Umbrella Stand $300.00-400.00
Florentine, Umbrella Stand $400.00-500.00

Pine Cone, Umbrella Stand $900.00-1,200.00
Florentine II, Sand Jar..$275.00-325.00
Bottom, left:
Lamp..$225.00-325.00
Bottom, right:
Vase, 8", No. 796 ....$100.00-125.00
Square Vase, feet, questionable orgin
Vase, 8", No. 942 ....$50.00-60.00
Bottom, center:
Basket, 10", No. C1012 (Capri) $75.00-100.00
Center, right:
Vista Basket, 8" $250.00-300.00

Second Series

Page 9, Rozane, 1900's
Row 1:
1. Vase, 12"..$400.00-500.00
2. Vase, 7"..$350.00-450.00
3. Vase, 5"..$275.00-375.00
Row 1:
Bottom:
1. Vase, 9½"...$1,800.00-2,000.00
2. Pillow Vase, 8½" $1,800.00-2,000.00
3. Vase, 8½"...$2,000.00-2,250.00
Row 2:
1. Vase, 9"..$2,000.00-2,250.00
2. Vase, 8"..$2,000.00-2,250.00
3. Vase, 9"..$1,800.00-2,000.00
Row 3:
1. Vase, 13"..$3,500.00-4,000.00
2. Vase, 17"..$3,000.00-3,500.00
3. Vase, 14"..$2,800.00-3,250.00

Page 11, Rozane, 1900's
Row 1:
1. Vase, 5½"..$175.00-200.00
2. Vase, 6½"..$125.00-150.00
3. Vase, 9"...$150.00-175.00
4. Vase, 8"...$150.00-175.00
5. Pillow Vase, 5" $150.00-175.00
Row 2:
1. Ewer, 7½" $150.00-175.00
2. Vase, 10"...$150.00-175.00
3. Vase, 13"...$200.00-275.00
4. Vase, 11"...$175.00-200.00
5. Ewer, 7½" $150.00-175.00
Row 3:
1. Vase, 10½"..$175.00-225.00
2. Paperweight..$200.00-225.00
3. Jardiniere, 9½" $150.00-200.00
4. Vase, 11"...$225.00-275.00

Page 12, Rozane, 1900's
Row 1:
1. Vase, 7"..$150.00-175.00
2. Tankard, 10½"...$225.00-300.00
3. Candlestick, 9"...$175.00-225.00
4. Vase, 7½"..$150.00-175.00
Row 2:
1. Vase, 8"..$2,000.00-2,250.00
2. Pillow Vase, 9"..$2,000.00-2,250.00
3. Vase, 7½"..$175.00-200.00
Row 3:
1. Vase, 14"..$2,750.00-3,000.00
2. Vase, 15"..$425.00-525.00
3. Vase, 14"..$450.00-550.00

Bottom, left:
1. Vase, 15"..$550.00-650.00
2. Vase, 10"..$900.00-1,000.00
3. Mug, 5...$900.00-1,100.00

Page 13, Rozane, 1900's
Row 1:
1. Letter Holder, 3½" $175.00-200.00
2. Mug, 4½"..$175.00-200.00
3. Bud Vase, 6½"..$150.00-175.00
4. Bud Vase, 6½"..$80.00-100.00
5. Mug, 5"..$150.00-175.00
6. Mug, 4½"..$150.00-175.00
Row 2:
1. Vase, 10"..$400.00-500.00
2. Vase, 11"..$325.00-425.00
3. Ewer, 10½"..$275.00-300.00
Row 3:
1. Vase, 13"..$250.00-300.00
2. Tankard, 14"...$250.00-325.00
3. Vase, 18½"..$375.00-450.00
4. Vase, 15"..$400.00-500.00
5. Vase, 10½"..$375.00-475.00

Page 14, Rozane, 1900's
Top:
Roseville Sign $1,200.00-1,500.00
Row 1:
1. Bud Vase, 7½"..$110.00-140.00
2. Bud Vase, 8"..$110.00-140.00
3. Pillow Vase, 7"..$275.00-325.00
4. Vase, 8½"..$150.00-175.00
5. Vase, 6½"..$125.00-150.00
Row 2:
1. Vase, 8½"..$125.00-150.00
2. Vase, 10½"..$175.00-225.00
3. Pillow Vase, 8½"..$300.00-350.00
4. Vase, 11"..$175.00-225.00
5. Vase, 10½"..$175.00-200.00
Row 3:
1. Vase, 14"..$400.00-500.00
2. Ewer, 16"..$375.00-450.00
3. Tankard, 15½"..$425.00-475.00
4. Mug, 6...$200.00-225.00

Page 15, Rozane, 1900's
Row 1:
1. Vase, 8"..$150.00-175.00
2. Vase, 9½"..$125.00-150.00
3. Vase, 11½"..$200.00-225.00
4. Chocolate Pot, 9½" $375.00-450.00

Row 2:
 1. Mug, 4"...$125.00-150.00
 2. Mug, 6"...$175.00-200.00
 3. Pillow Vase, 7".....................................$200.00-250.00
 4. Mug, 4"...$125.00-150.00
Row 3:
 1. Tankard, 16"...$450.00-500.00
 2. Vase, 16"...$300.00-350.00
 3. Tankard, 15½".......................................$300.00-350.00

Page 16, Light Rozane
Row 1:
 1. Bowl, 3"..$150.00-175.00
 2. Vase, 4"..$175.00-200.00
 3. Bowl, 5"..$125.00-150.00
 4. Mug, 5"..$250.00-300.00
Row 2:
 1. Pillow Vase, 6½"...................................$275.00-325.00
 2. Vase, 8½"..$1,250.00-1,500.00
 3. Pillow Vase, 7"....................................$300.00-375.00
Row 3:
 1. Vase, 6½"..$275.00-325.00
 2. Vase, 13"...$350.00-450.00
 3. Vase, 18".......................................$900.00-1,100.00
 4. Vase, 14"...$850.00-950.00
 5. Vase, 8½"..$325.00-375.00
Bottom:
 1. Jardiniere, 5".......................................$125.00-150.00
 2. Vase, 11½"...$250.00-300.00
 3. Vase, 15".......................................$900.00-1,000.00

Page 17, Light Rozane
Row 1:
 1. Sugar Bowl, 4½"...................................$175.00-200.00
 2. Teapot, 6".......................................$1,100.00-1,250.00
 3. Mug, 5"...$250.00-275.00
Row 2:
 1. Vase, 8"..$275.00-325.00
 2. Vase, 8"..$275.00-325.00
 3. Vase, 10"..$375.00-425.00
 4. Vase, 10"..$300.00-350.00
 5. Vase, 8½"..$275.00-325.00
Row 3:
 1. Tankard, 11".......................................$425.00-475.00
 2. Vase, 11"...$300.00-350.00
 3. Tankard, 16".......................................$575.00-675.00
 4. Vase, 10½"...$275.00-350.00
 5. Tankard, 10".......................................$375.00-425.00

Page 18, Paper Collectibles
 Stationery Items, Cards $20.00-35.00

Page 19, Vase Assortment #24; Azurean, 1902
Top:
 1. Vase, 8"..$300.00-325.00
 2. Vase, 9"..$325.00-375.00
 3. Vase, 9"..$325.00-375.00
 4. Vase, 8"..$325.00-375.00
 5. Vase, 7"..$275.00-325.00
Bottom:
 1. Vase, 9".......................................$1,800.00-1,900.00
Row 2:
 1. Candlestick, 9"....................................$475.00-575.00
 2. Vase, 7½"..$475.00-575.00
 3. Mug, 5"...$425.00-475.00
Row 3:
 1. Vase, 14".......................................$1,100.00-1,250.00
 2. Vase, 18".......................................$1,000.00-1,250.00
 3. Vase, 15½"....................................$1,000.00-1,150.00

Page 21, Olympic, 1905; Mara, 1904
Top Row 1:
 1. Pitcher, 7".....................................$2,000.00-2,250.00
 2. Pitcher, 7".....................................$1,850.00-2,150.00
Row 2:
 1. Vase, 14½"....................................$3,500.00-4,000.00
 2. Vase, 20".......................................$4,000.00-4,500.00
Bottom left:
 1. Vase, 13".......................................$1,500.00-1,800.00
 2. Bowl, 4"..$1,100.00-1,300.00
 3. Vase, 13".......................................$1,500.00-2,000.00
Bottom right:
 1. Vase, 5½"......................................$1,400.00-1,750.00
 2. Vase, 5½"......................................$1,300.00-1,650.00

Page 23, Mongol, 1904
Top, Row 1:
 1. Mug, 6"...$700.00-850.00
 2. Vase, 5"..$500.00-600.00
Row 2:
 1. Vase, 10½".....................................$1,100.00-1,250.00
 2. Vase, 14"...$900.00-1,100.00
 3. Vase, 16"...$900.00-1,150.00
Bottom, left:
 1. Vase, 8"..$800.00-900.00
 2. Vase, 10½"...$850.00-950.00
Bottom, right:
 1. Vase, 7".......................................$2,200.00-2,500.00
 2. Vase, 2½"..$400.00-500.00

Page 24, Woodland, 1905
Row 1:
 1. Vase, 6"..$550.00-650.00
 2. Vase, 6½"..$575.00-650.00
 3. Vase, 6½"..$575.00-650.00
 4. Vase, 7"..$550.00-600.00
Row 2:
 1. Vase, 9"..$650.00-750.00
 2. Vase, 9"..$650.00-750.00
 3. Vase, 11"..$700.00-900.00
 4. Vase, 11½"...$750.00-950.00
 5. Vase, 10"..$700.00-800.00
 6. Vase, 9"..$600.00-700.00
Row 3:
 1. Vase, 13".......................................$1,200.00-1,500.00
 2. Vase, 19".......................................$1,800.00-2,200.00
 3. Vase, 15½"....................................$1,000.00-1,200.00
 4. Vase, 15".......................................$1,100.00-1,300.00

Page 25, Fudji, 1906; Fujiyama, 1906
Top, right:
 1. Vase, 6".......................................$1,000.00-1,250.00
 2. Pitcher, 7½"...................................$1,100.00-1,300.00
 3. Woodland Vase, 11"..........................$1,800.00-2,000.00
Bottom, Row 1:
 1. Vase, 9".......................................$1,250.00-1,500.00
 2. Vase, 10½"....................................$1,300.00-1,500.00
 3. Vase, 10".......................................$1,300.00-1,450.00
Row 2:
 1. Vase, 15".......................................$1,000.00-1,250.00
 2. Jardiniere, 9".................................$1,100.00-1,350.00
 3. Vase, 11"...$850.00-950.00
 4. Vase, 9"..$750.00-850.00

Page 26, Della Robbia, 1906
Row 1:
 1. Teapot, 6".....................................$1,100.00-1,300.00
 2. Teapot, 5½"...................................$1,100.00-1,500.00
 3. Teapot, 6".....................................$1,100.00-1,250.00

Row 2:
1. Mug, 4½" $500.00-750.00
2. Pitcher, 8" $3,500.00-4,500.00
3. Mug, 4½" $500.00-750.00
Bottom, Row 1:
1. Tankard, 10½" $1,700.00-2,100.00
2. Teapot, 6½" $1,200.00-1,300.00
3. Tankard, 10½" $1,350.00-1,550.00
Row 2:
1. Vase, 10" $3,500.00-4,500.00
2. Vase, 11" $2,500.00-2,750.00
3. Vase, 9" $1,500.00-2,000.00

Page 27, Della Robbia, 1906
Row 1:
1. Vase, 8" $3,250.00-4,000.00
2. Teapot, 8" $1,200.00-1,500.00
3. Vase, 8½" $3,000.00-4,000.00
Row 2:
1. Mug, 4" (no lid) $500.00-700.00
2. Vase, 8" $2,250.00-2,500.00
3. Vase, 9½" $1,250.00-1,750.00
4. Bowl, 8" $1,300.00-1,500.00
5. Letter Holder, 3½" $650.00-750.00
Row 3:
1. Vase, 15" $5,000.00-6,000.00
2. Vase, 14" $6,000.00-8,000.00
3. Vase, 11½" $6,000.00-8,000.00
4. Vase, 11½" $3,000.00-4,000.00
Bottom left:
Vase, 19" $6,000.00-8,000.00
Bottom, center:
Vase, 12" $8,000.00-12,000.00
Bottom, right:
Vase, 8½" $4,000.00-5,000.00

Page 28, Crystalis, 1906
1. Vase, 14" $1,200.00-1,400.00
2. Pot, 3" $900.00-1,100.00

Page 29, Crystalis, 1906
Top:
1. Candlestick, 9" $800.00-900.00
2. Vase, 12½" $1,300.00-1,500.00
3. Vase, 13" $1,250.00-1,500.00
4. Vase, 11" $1,300.00-1,450.00
5. Vase, 5½" $800.00-900.00
Bottom, Row 1:
1. Vase, 3½" $350.00-450.00
2. Planter, 4" $300.00-400.00
3. Vase, 7", (Arc-En-Ciel) $250.00-350.00
4. Vase, 5½" $600.00-800.00
Row 2:
1. Vase, 11" $900.00-1,100.00
2. Vase, 9" $1,000.00-1,300.00
3. Vase, 8½" $500.00-800.00
4. Weller
5. Vase, 12" $400.00-500.00
Row 3: Blue Teapots
1. Mug, 6" $175.00-200.00
2. Pot, 8" $200.00-250.00
3. Pot, 7" $300.00-350.00
4. Pot, 4" $200.00-250.00

Page 30, Special, Early 1900's
1. Mug, 5" $125.00-150.00
2. Tankard, 12" $250.00-300.00
3. Mug, 5" $125.00-150.00
4. Tankard, 15½" $250.00-300.00

Page 31, Decorated Art
Row 1:
1. Jardiniere, 8" $225.00-325.00
2. Vase, 12½" $325.00-425.00
3. Jardiniere, 6" $175.00-225.00
Row 2:
1. Jardiniere, 10" $250.00-300.00
2. Vase, 16" $800.00-1,000.00
Bottom:
1. Pillow Vase, 9" $3,000.00-3,500.00
2. Vase, 9" $350.00-450.00

Page 32, Egypto, 1905; Chloron, 1907; Matt Green, before 1916
Top:
Hanging Basket $150.00-200.00
Row 1:
1. Planter/Liner, 4" $125.00-150.00
2. Candlestick, 4" $150.00-175.00
3. 3-Way Creamer, 3½" $175.00-200.00
4. Bud Vase, 5½" $150.00-175.00
5. Bowl, 3" $150.00-175.00
Row 2:
1. Jardiniere, 5½" $110.00-135.00
2. Vase, 7" $375.00-475.00
3. Vase, 9" $375.00-500.00
Row 3:
1. Vase, 12½" $350.00-450.00
2. Pitcher, 12" $300.00-350.00
3. Jug, 11" $450.00-500.00
4. Planter, 5½" $125.00-175.00

Page 33, Egypto, Matt Green, Chloron
Row 1:
1. Vase, 6½" $150.00-200.00
2. Vase, 12" $350.00-450.00
3. Vase, 9" $350.00-450.00
Row 2:
1. Pot/liner, 3" $40.00-50.00
2. Pot/liner, 3" $45.00-50.00
3. Pot/liner, 4" $40.00-50.00
4. Gate $35.00-50.00
5. Pot/Frog, 2½" $40.00-50.00
Row 3:
1. Jardiniere, 6" $100.00-125.00
2. Tobacco Jar, 6" $150.00-200.00
3. Planter/Liner, 4" $150.00-250.00
4. Jardiniere, 5½" $150.00-250.00
Row 4:
1. Pitcher, 11" $225.00-250.00
2. Lamp Base, 10" $600.00-800.00
3. Vase, 6½" $125.00-175.00
4. Pitcher, 7" $175.00-200.00
5. Vase, 5½" $150.00-200.00

Page 35, Pauleo, 1914
Row 1:
1. Vase, 9" $500.00-600.00
2. Vase, 12" $500.00-650.00
3. Vase, 9" $500.00-600.00
Row 2:
1. Vase, 18½" $1,000.00-1,250.00
2. Vase, 19" $1,100.00-1,250.00
3. Vase, 20½" $1,200.00-1,400.00

Page 36, Pauleo, 1914
Row 1:
1. Vase, 17" $1,000.00-1,200.00
2. Vase, 14" $900.00-1,000.00
Row 2:
1. Vase, 17½" $1,000.00-1,200.00
2. Vase, 19" $1,150.00-1,250.00
3. Vase, 16½" $950.00-1,150.00

Page 37, Pauleo, 1914
Row 1:
    1. Vase, 16½"..$950.00-1,150.00
    2. Vase, 14"..$900.00-1,100.00
    3. Vase, 16½"..$950.00-1,150.00
Row 2:
    1. Vase, 15½"..$1,100.00-1,300.00
    2. Vase, 17"..$1,100.00-1,350.00
Below, left:
    1. Vase, 12"..$1,200.00-1,500.00
    2. Vase, 12'..$600.00-750.00
Below, right:
    1. Vase, 19"..$1,200.00-1,300.00
    2. Bowl, 3"..$400.00-500.00
    3. Vase, 19"..$1,150.00-1,250.00

Page 38, Cornelian, Colonial, Holland
Row 1:
    1. Shaving Mug, 4"......................................$65.00-75.00
    2. Mush Bowl & Pitcher................................$80.00-100.00
    3. Toothbrush, 5".......................................$60.00-70.00
    4. Soap Dish, 4"...$75.00-85.00
Row 2:
    1. Soap Dish, 4"...$80.00-90.00
    2. Salesman's Sample $70.00-80.00
    3. Shaving Mug, 4"......................................$65.00-75.00
    4. Pitcher, 12"..$250.00-350.00
Row 3:
    1. Pitcher & Bowl $350.00-450.00
    2. Combinet, 12"......................................$300.00-350.00

Page 39, Cornelian Colonial, Holland
Row 1:
    1. Pitcher, 4"..$50.00-60.00
    2. Pitcher, 5"..$50.00-60.00
    3. Pitcher, 9"..$80.00-100.00
    4. Pitcher, 5½"...$60.00-70.00
    5. Pitcher, 5"..$65.00-75.00
Row 2:
    1. Pitcher, 6"..$75.00-100.00
    2. Jardiniere, 4½" $75.00-90.00
    3. Jardiniere, 4"..$65.00-75.00
Row 3:
    1. Pitcher, 7½"..$80.00-100.00
    2. Pitcher, 11"...$175.00-250.00
        Bowl, 11"..$150.00-200.00
    3. Toothbrush...$65.00-85.00
Bottom:
    1. Powder jar, 3"..$85.00-95.00
    2. Tankard, 9½".......................................$125.00-175.00
    3. Pitcher, 6½"...$125.00-150.00
    4. Mug, 4"..$45.00-55.00

Page 41, Aztec, Crocus
Row 1:
    1. Vase, 11½" $350.00-450.00
    2. Vase, 10½"..$300.00-400.00
    3. Vase, 9½"..$225.00-275.00
Row 2:
    1. Vase, 7"...$300.00-350.00
    2. Vase, 9½"..$425.00-475.00
    3. Vase, 9"...$375.00-425.00
    4. Same as #1
Row 3:
    1. Vase, 9"...$350.00-400.00
    2. Vase, 7"...$350.00-400.00
    3. Vase, 6"...$300.00-350.00
    4. Letter Receiver, 3½"...............................$200.00-250.00
Row 4:
    1. Vase, 9"...$425.00-475.00
    2. Vase, 11"..$400.00-500.00

    3. Vase, 11"..$400.00-500.00
    4. Vase, 9"..$375.00-425.00
    5. Vase, 8"..$400.00-500.00

Page 42, Early Pitchers
Row 1:
    1. Pitcher, 6½"...$60.00-75.00
    2. Pitcher, 8"...$65.00-85.00
Row 2:
    1. Pitcher, 6"..$80.00-110.00
    2. Pitcher, 7½"...$275.00-375.00
    3. Pitcher, 6"..$80.00-110.00
Row 3:
    1. Pitcher, 9½"...$110.00-125.00
    2. Pitcher, 8"...$275.00-325.00
    3. Pitcher, 9½"...$100.00-125.00

Page 43, Early Pitchers
Row 1:
    1. Pitcher, 6"...$125.00-150.00
    2. Pitcher, 7"...$150.00-200.00
    3. Pitcher, 6"...$125.00-150.00
Row 2:
    1. Pitcher, 7½"...$125.00-150.00
    2. Pitcher, 7½"...$100.00-125.00
    3. Pitcher, 7½"...$125.00-150.00
Row 3:
    1. Pitcher, 7½"...$300.00-350.00
    2. Pitcher, 6½"...$300.00-400.00
    3. Pitcher, 7½"...$300.00-350.00
Bottom:
    1. Pitcher, 9"...$125.00-150.00
    2. Pitcher, 9"...$125.00-150.00

Page 44, Blended Glazed and Early Pitchers
Row 1:
    1. Vase, 7"...$75.00-100.00
    2. Tankard, 12".......................................$125.00-150.00
    3. Vase, 6½"..$60.00-75.00
Row 2:
    1. Pitcher, 3"..$40.00-50.00
    2. Vase, 3"..$40.00-50.00
    3. Vase, 5½"..$40.00-50.00
    4. Vase, 4"..$40.00-50.00
Row 3:
    1. Pitcher, 6½"...$300.00-400.00
    2. Pitcher, 7"...$100.00-125.00
    3. Pitcher, 6"...$100.00-125.00
Row 4:
    1. Pitcher, 7½"...$125.00-150.00
    2. Pitcher, 9"...$100.00-125.00
    3. Pitcher, 9½"...$150.00-200.00
    4. Pitcher, 8½"...$300.00-400.00
Bottom, Row 1:
    1. Apple Band $125.00-150.00
Row 2:
    1. Apple Band $125.00-150.00
    2. Orange Bank......................................$125.00-150.00

Page 45, Banks
Row 1:
    1. Pig..$125.00-150.00
    2. Large Pig $150.00-200.00
    3. Pig..$125.00-175.00
Row 2:
    1. Buffalo..$150.00-200.00
    2. Dog $150.00-200.00
    3. Uncle Sam $125.00-150.00
    4. Buffalo..$150.00-200.00

Center, Row 1:
- 1. Jug $75.00-100.00
- 2. Monkey bottle $100.00-125.00
- 3. Monkey $125.00-150.00
- 4. Monkey $100.00-125.00

Row 2:
- 1. Eagle $150.00-175.00
- 2. Lion $100.00-125.00
- 3. Cat $150.00-175.00
- 4. Beehive $175.00-200.00
- 5. Beehive $150.00-175.00

Page 46, Tourist
Vase, 9" $500.00-600.00

Page 47, Cremo, Sylvan, Tourist, Autumn
Upper left:
Vase, 7" $800.00-950.00
Upper right:
- 1. Vase, 9½" $275.00-325.00
- 2. Jardiniere, 9" $250.00-300.00

Center:
- 1. Window Box, 8½" $1,200.00-1,500.00
- 2. Vase, 8" $650.00-750.00

Bottom, Row 1:
- 1. Pitcher, 8½" $320.00-400.00
- 2. Toothbrush, 5" $225.00-275.00
- 3. Shaving Mug, 4" $225.00-275.00
- 4. Soap Dish/Liner, 5½" $250.00-300.00

Row 2:
- 1. Wash Bowl, 14½" $300.00-375.00
  Pitcher, 12½" $450.00-500.00
  Set $750.00-850.00
- 2. Jardiniere, 9½" $500.00-600.00

Page 48, Smoker Sets
Row 1:
- 1. Ashtray, 2" $45.00-50.00
- 2. Ashtray, 3" $150.00-175.00
- 3. Indian Smoker Set $275.00-300.00
- 4. Ashtray, 2" $45.00-50.00

Row 2:
Ashtrays, 2", each $45.00-50.00

Page 49, Novelty Steins
Choice $175.00-225.00
Bottom: Smoker Sets
- 1. Tobacco Jar, 6" $200.00-250.00
- 2. Combination Set $300.00-350.00
- 3. Combination Set $250.00-275.00
- 4. Jar, 4½" $125.00-150.00

Page 50, Donatella Tea Sets
Row 1:
Set $325.00-350.00
Creamer...$60.00-70.00
Sugar with lid $70.00-80.00

Row 2:
Set $275.00-300.00
Creamer...$60.00-70.00
Sugar with lid $70.00-80.00

Row 3:
Set $300.00-325.00
Creamer...$60.00-70.00
Sugar with lid $70.00-80.00

Row 4:
Set $250.00-275.00
Creamer...$45.00-55.00
Sugar with lid $55.00-65.00

Row 5:
Set $375.00-400.00
Creamer...$75.00-90.00
Sugar with lid $100.00-110.00

Page 51
Row 1:
Creamer...$60.00-70.00
Teapot $150.00-175.00
Chocolate Pot $175.00-200.00
Sugar $70.00-80.00

Row 2:
- 1. Creamer $45.00-55.00
- 2. Sugar $55.00-65.00
- 3. Candlestick, 7" $300.00-350.00
- 4. Pitcher, 5" $75.00-100.00

Row 3:
- 1. Pot/Liner, 3½" $65.00-75.00
- 2. Pot/Liner, 4" $150.00-175.00
- 3. Pot/Liner, 4" $50.00-60.00
- 4. Pot/Liner, 3½" $75.00-85.00

Row 4:
- 1. Teapot, 8½" $300.00-350.00
- 2. Trivet, 6" $85.00-110.00
- 3. Pitcher, 8" $150.00-175.00

Page 52, Gold Traced and Decorated and Gold Traced
Above:
- 1. Candlestick, 9" $85.00-110.00
- 2. Candlestick, 9" $85.00-110.00
- 3. Candlestick, 4" $50.00-75.00
- 4. Candlestick, 9" $100.00-125.00
- 5. Candlestick, 8½" $100.00-125.00

Below, Dutch
Row 1:
- 1. Mug, 4" $65.00-75.00
- 2. Pitcher, 7½" 120.00-140.00
- 3. Teapot, 4½" $75.00-100.00

Row 2:
- 1. Pin Tray, 4" $50.00-60.00
- 2. Teapot, 6½" $175.00-210.00
- 3. Toothbrush, 4" $50.00-60.00

Page 53, Dutch
Row 1:
Creamer...$50.00-70.00
Teapot $100.00-125.00
Sugar $50.00-75.00

Row 2:
- 1. Soap Dish/Lid $125.00-150.00
- 2. Milk Pitcher, 4½" $125.00-150.00
- 3. Tumbler, 4" $100.00-110.00
- 4. Tumbler, 4" $100.00-125.00

Row 3:
- 1. Humidor, 6" $200.00-250.00
- 2. Plate, 11" $100.00-125.00
- 3. Creamer, 3" $60.00-75.00
- 4. Teapot, 7" $175.00-225.00

Row 4:
- 1. Combinet, 10½" $225.00-275.00
- 2. Child's Potty, 5½" $200.00-250.00
- 3. Tankard, 11½" $125.00-150.00

Page 54
Row 1:
- 1. Mug, 5" $95.00-125.00
- 2. Mug, 5" $225.00-275.00
- 3. Mug, 5" $250.00-275.00
- 4. Mug, 5" $100.00-125.00

Row 2:
    1. Custard Cup, 2½" $50.00-60.00
    2. Tumbler, 4" $100.00-125.00
    3. Jardiniere/Liner $85.00-95.00
    4. Jardiniere/Liner $85.00-95.00
    5. Mug, 3½" $150.00-175.00
Row 3:
    1. Pitcher, 6" $200.00-225.00
    2. Coffee Pot, 10" $275.00-325.00
    3. Teapot, 9" $175.00-225.00
Row 4:
    1. Mug, 5" $150.00-175.00
    2. Tankard, 11½" $300.00-350.00
    3. Mug, 5" $150.00-175.00
    4. Mug, 5" $150.00-175.00
    5. Tankard, 11½" $225.00-275.00
    6. Mug, 5" $90.00-110.00

Page 55, Stein Sets
Row 1:
    1. Mug, 5" $75.00-100.00
    2. Mug, 5" $225.00-275.00
    3. Mug, 5" $75.00-100.00
Row 2:
    Mugs, 5", each.....................................$175.00-200.00
Row 3:
    1. Mug, 5" $125.00-175.00
    2. Mug, 5" $150.00-175.00
    3. Tankard, 12" $250.00-300.00
    4. Tankard, 12" $175.00-225.00
    5. Mug, 5" $125.00-150.00
    6. Mug, 5" $150.00-175.00
Row 4:
    1. Tankard, 12" $175.00-225.00
    2. Tankard, 12" $400.00-450.00
    3. Tankard, 11½" $225.00-275.00
    4. Tankard, 10½" $300.00-350.00
    5. Tankard, 10½" $250.00-300.00

Page 56
    Watch Fob..$350.00-400.00
Below, Row 1:
    1. Tumbler, 4"..$150.00-175.00
    2. Pitcher, 3½" $40.00-50.00
    3. Creamer, 3" $55.00-65.00
    4. Creamer, 3½" $60.00-70.00
    5. Dish, 2" $90.00-100.00
Row 2:
    1. Toothbrush, 5".................................$150.00-175.00
    2. Mug, 5"..$75.00-100.00
    3. Mug, 5"..$75.00-100.00
    4. Mug, 5..$75.00-100.00
Row 3
    1. Dog Dish, 3" $75.00-90.00
    2. Dog Dish, 2" $75.00-90.00

Page 57
Row 1:
    1. Ring Tree, 3½" $70.00-80.00
    2. Pin Box, 4" $70.00-80.00
    3. Dresser Tray, 10" $125.00-150.00
    4. & 5. Candlesticks, 2" ....each $70.00-80.00
Row 2:
    1. Pitcher, 7"...$175.00-200.00
    2. Spittoon, 10" $275.00-300.00
    3. Flower Arranger, 2 piece................$60.00-70.00
    4. Flower Arranger, 2 piece................$60.00-70.00

Row 3:
    1. Tankard, 12" $225.00-275.00
    2. Mug, 5" $150.00-175.00
    3. Tankard, 11½" $300.00-350.00
    4. Mug, 5" $150.00-175.00
    5. Tankard, 11½" $250.00-275.00

Page 58
Bottom, left:
    1. Comport, 9" $150.00-200.00
    2. Pot, 3½" $60.00-80.00
Bottom, right:
    Sugar, 3" $50.00-60.00
    Creamer, 1½" $50.00-60.00

Page 59, Old Ivory, Ivory Tints
Row 1:
    1. Planter, 4" $50.00-60.00
    2. Humidor, 6" $150.00-225.00
    3. Double Bud Vase $75.00-85.00
Row 2:
    1. Jardiniere/Liner, 8" $175.00-200.00
    2. Tankard, 13½" $200.00-250.00
    3. Jardiniere, 9" $150.00-175.00
Center:
    1. Pot, 8" $150.00-175.00
    2. Plate, 8" $325.00-375.00
    3. Coffee Pot, 10" $185.00-225.00
Bottom:
    1. Candlestick, 7" $350.00-400.00
    2. Teapot, 4½" $200.00-250.00
    3. Creamer, 3" $100.00-125.00
    4. Reverse #1

Page 60, Persian, Ceramic Design
Top:
    1. Jardiniere, 5" $150.00-175.00
    2. Hanging Basket $225.00-250.00
    3. Jardiniere, 8" $225.00-250.00
Center:
    1. Jardiniere, 6½" $125.00-150.00
    2. Candlestick, 8½" $125.00-150.00
    3. Jardiniere, 5" $100.00-125.00
Below:
    Tumblers, 4", each $60.00-80.00
    Pitcher, 6½" $175.00-200.00

Page 61
Row 1:
    1. Spittoon, 5" $75.00-100.00
    2. Spittoon, 5" $125.00-150.00
    3. Spittoon, 5" $100.00-125.00
Row 2:
    1. Jardiniere, 8" $500.00-600.00
    2. Jardiniere, 8" $100.00-150.00
Row 3:
    1. Jardiniere, 9" $550.00-650.00
    2. Jardiniere, 8" $550.00-650.00
Bottom:
    1. Jardiniere, 4½" $40.00-50.00
    2. Jard. and Ped. 12" $175.00-225.00
    3. Jardiniere, 5½" $55.00-70.00
Page 62
Row 1:
    1. Bake Pan 7" $25.00-35.00
    2. Pudding Crock $30.00-40.00

3. Bake Pan, 9"................................$25.00-30.00

Center, Row 1:
   1. Pitcher, 6½"................................$85.00-95.00
   2. Bowl, 5½"................................$40.00-45.00
   3. Pitcher, 6½"................................$85.00-95.00

Row 2:
   1. Pitcher, 7½"................................$75.00-100.00
   2. Pitcher, 7½"................................$50.00-75.00
   3. Pitcher, 6"................................$50.00-75.00

Below, Row 1:
   1. Bake Pan, 3"................................$30.00-40.00
   2. Pitcher, 8"................................$50.00-60.00

Row 2:
   1. Mug, 3½"................................$40.00-45.00
   2. Mug, 4"................................$40.00-45.00
   3. Mug, 5"................................$40.00-45.00
   4. Mug, 6"................................$40.00-45.00
   5. Pitcher................................$50.00-60.00

Page 63, Juvenile

Row 1:
   Sugar................................$100.00-125.00
   Pot................................$200.00-225.00
   Creamer................................$75.00-100.00

Row 2:
   1. Creamer, 3½"................................$150.00-200.00
   2. Plate, 8"................................$300.00-350.00
   3. Cup and saucer................................$175.00-225.00

Row 3:
   1. Mug, 3"................................$60.00-75.00
   2. Plate, 8"................................$125.00-150.00
   3. Egg Cup, 4"................................$175.00-225.00

Row 4:
   1. Plate, 8"................................$175.00-250.00
   2. Creamer, 4"................................$125.00-150.00
   3. Plate, 8"................................$200.00-250.00

Row 5:
   1. Divided Plate, 8½"................................$250.00-300.00
   2. Plate, 8"................................$175.00-225.00
   3. Plate, 8"................................$175.00-225.00
   4. Mug, 3"................................$125.00-150.00

Page 64, Juvenile

Row 1:
   1. Mug, 3½"................................$100.00-125.00
   2. Pitcher, 3½"................................$100.00-150.00
   3. Plate, 7"................................$150.00-200.00
   4. Creamer, 3½"................................$100.00-150.00
   5. Bowl, 4½"................................$125.00-175.00

Row 2:
   1. Creamer, 3"................................$75.00-100.00
   2. Bowl, 5"................................$75.00-100.00
   3. Plate, 8"................................$125.00-175.00
   4. Bowl, 6"................................$100.00-125.00
   5. Creamer, 3"................................$75.00-100.00

Row 3:
   1. Custard, 2½"................................$50.00-75.00
   2. Creamer, 3"................................$75.00-100.00
   3. Plate, 7"................................$125.00-150.00
   4. Pitcher, 3"................................$75.00-100.00
      Bowl................................$100.00-125.00
   5. Cup, saucer................................$125.00-150.00

Row 4:
   1. Plate, 8"................................$125.00-150.00
   2. Egg Cup, 3½"................................$125.00-225.00
   3. Cake Plate, 9½"................................$150.00-200.00

   4. Pudding Dish, 3½"................................$75.00-100.00
   5. Plate, 7"................................$100.00-125.00

Page 65, Juvenile

Row 1:
   1. Creamer, 4"................................$150.00-200.00
   2. Bowl, 6"................................$150.00-200.00
   3. Mug, 3½"................................$175.00-225.00

Row 2:
   1. Cup, Saucer................................$125.00-150.00
   2. Teapot, 4"................................$175.00-225.00
   3. Sugar, 3"................................$100.00-125.00

Row 3:
   1. Mug, 3½"................................$125.00-150.00
   2. Plate, 7"................................$125.00-150.00
   3. Creamer, 4"................................$100.00-125.00
   4. Custard, 2½"................................$75.00-100.00

Row 4:
   1. Custard, 2½"................................$100.00-125.00
   2. Pitcher................................$75.00-100.00
      Bowl................................$75.00-100.00
   3. Creamer, 3½"................................$75.00-100.00
   4. Cup, Saucer................................$100.00-125.00
   5. Pudding Dish, 1½"................................$75.00-90.00

Row 5:
   1. Egg Cup, 3"................................$150.00-200.00
   2. Plate, 7"................................$100.00-125.00
   3. Plate, 8"................................$100.00-125.00
   4. Plate, 7"................................$100.00-125.00
   5. Egg Cup, 3½"................................$150.00-200.00

Page 66, Juvenile and Nursery

Row 1:
   1. Creamer, 3"................................$100.00-150.00
   2. Teapot, 5"................................$175.00-250.00
   3. Sugar, 4"................................$100.00-150.00

Row 2 & 3:
   Plates, 8", each................................$175.00-225.00

Center:
   Pitcher, 7½"................................$350.00-450.00
   Bowl, 10½"................................$350.00-400.00

Page 67, Juvenile

Row 1:
   1. Mug, 3"................................$75.00-100.00
   2. Plate, 8"................................$125.00-150.00
   3. Cup, Saucer................................$125.00-175.00
   4. Plate, 8"................................$125.00-150.00
   5. Creamer, 3½"................................$75.00-100.00

Row 2:
   1. Creamer, 3½"................................$75.00-100.00
   2. Cup, Saucer................................$125.00-175.00
   3. Plate, 8"................................$125.00-150.00
   4. Plate, 8"................................$125.00-150.00
   5. Mug, 3"................................$75.00-110.00
   6. Mug, 3"................................$75.00-100.00

Row 3:
   1. Creamer, 3½"................................$75.00-100.00
   2. Cup, Saucer................................$125.00-175.00
   3. Plate, 8"................................$125.00-175.00
   4. Plate, 8"................................$125.00-175.00
   5. Egg Cup, 4"................................$150.00-200.00
   6. Mug, 3"................................$75.00-110.00

Row 4:
   1. Mug, 3"................................$150.00-200.00
   2. Boxed Set................................$350.00-450.00
   3. Potty................................$225.00-275.00
   Add $100.00 for lid.

Page 69, Carnelian I
Row 1:
    1. Bowl/Frog, 3" $50.00-75.00
    2. Vase, 8" $50.00-60.00
    3. Fan Vase, 6" $40.00-50.00
    4. Bowl, 3" $40.00-50.00
Row 2:
    1. Candleholder/Frog $35.00-45.00
    2. Pillow Vase, 5" $40.00-50.00
    3. Console, 5" $60.00-75.00
    4. Flower Frog $30.00-40.00
Row 3:
    1. Urn, 7" $60.00-80.00
    2. Vase, 8" $70.00-80.00
    3. Vase, 7" $70.00-80.00
    4. Urn, 8" $80.00-100.00
Row 4:
    1. Urn, 9½" $100.00-125.00
    2. Vase, 10" $100.00-125.00
    3. Urn, 10" $125.00-150.00

Page 71, Carnelian II
Row 1:
    1. Urn, 5" $125.00-150.00
    2. Vase, 7" $125.00-165.00
    3. Planter, 3" $65.00-80.00
Row 2:
    1. Urn, 8" $150.00-200.00
    2. Urn, 6" $200.00-300.00
    3. Urn, 8" $150.00-200.00
Row 3:
    1. Vase, 7" $90.00-125.00
    2. Ewer, 12½" $125.00-175.00
    3. Vase, 10" $100.00-150.00
    4. Vase, 8" $100.00-140.00

Page 72, Carnelian II
Row 1:
    1. Vase, 12" $450.00-550.00
    2. Vase, 15" $600.00-800.00
    3. Vase, 12" $450.00-550.00
Row 2:
    1. Vase, 12" $450.00-550.00
    2. Lamp Base, 8" $250.00-300.00
    3. Vase, 14" $550.00-700.00
Bottom, right:
    1. Vase, 18½" $650.00-850.00
    2. Vase, 14½" $550.00-750.00

Page 73, Carnelian II
Row 1:
    1. Vase, 8" $100.00-150.00
    2. Basket, 4" $200.00-300.00
    3. Vase, 7" $75.00-100.00
Row 2:
    1. Bowl, 3" $40.00-60.00
    2. Bowl, 5" $125.00-175.00
    3. Fan Vase, 6½" $40.00-60.00
Row 3:
    1. Bowl, Rare 4" $175.00-225.00
    2. Bowl, Rare 4" $200.00-250.00
Row 4:
    1. Vase, 9" $125.00-175.00
    2. Vase, 9" $125.00-175.00

    3. Vase, 8" $100.00-150.00
    4. Frog, 4" $50.00-75.00

Page 74
Below, right:
    Jardiniere $150.00-200.00
    Metal Stand $200.00-250.00

Page 75, Mostique
    Hanging Basket, 7" $150.00-225.00
Row 1:
    1. Bowl, 7" $40.00-50.00
    2. Bowl, 7" $40.00-50.00
    3. Bowl, 5½" $35.00-45.00
Row 2:
    1. Bowl, 9½" $60.00-70.00
    2. Comport, 7" $75.00-125.00
    3. Bowl, 9" $75.00-100.00
Row 3:
    1. Vase, 10" $125.00-175.00
    2. Vase, 12" $175.00-250.00
    3. Jardiniere, 8" $100.00-150.00
    4. Vase, 6" $50.00-75.00

Page 76, Rosecraft Panel
Row 1:
    1. Vase, 6" $75.00-100.00
    2. Covered jar, 10" $300.00-350.00
    3. Urn, 4" $50.00-80.00
Row 2:
    1. Lamp Base, 10" $200.00-275.00
    2. Window Box, 6" $150.00-250.00
    3. Vase, 10" $175.00-225.00

Page 77, Imperial I
Row 1:
    1. Basket, 9" $100.00-125.00
    2. Basket, 10" $125.00-150.00
    3. Basket, 10" $125.00-150.00
    4. Vase, 8" $100.00-125.00
Row 2:
    1. Vase, 10" $150.00-200.00
    2. Comport, 6" $100.00-135.00
    3, Vase, 8" $125.00-175.00
Row 3:
    1. Vase, 10" $125.00-175.00
    2. Planter, 14" $100.00-150.00
    3. Vase, 12" $125.00-175.00

Page 78, Donatello
Row 1:
    1. Powder Jar, 2" $200.00-250.00
    2. Vase, 6" $125.00-150.00
    3. Double Bud Vase, 7" $175.00-225.00
    4. Incense Burner, 3½" $250.00-300.00
Row 2:
    1. Vase, 8½" $150.00-175.00
    2. Vase, 12" $175.00-200.00
    3. Vase, 9½" $125.00-150.00
    4. Plate, 8" $200.00-250.00
Bottom:
    Stencil $75.00-100.00
    Light Sconce $150.00-200.00

Page 79, Donatello
Row 1:
    1. Bowl, 6" $40.00-50.00

2. Ashtray, 3" $50.00-75.00
3. Hanging Basket, 7" $125.00-150.00
4. Ashtray, 3" $50.00-75.00
5. Ashtray, 2" $65.00-85.00
Row 2:
1. Bowl, 9½" $50.00-65.00
2. Bowl, 8½" $50.00-60.00
3. Bowl, 8" $50.00-60.00
Row 3:
1. Cuspidor, 5½" $165.00-195.00
2. Jardiniere, 6" $95.00-110.00
3. Comport, 5" $65.00-80.00
4. Candlestick, 6½" $70.00-80.00
Row 4:
1. Vase, 8" $40.00-50.00
2. Vase, 10" $70.00-80.00
3. Vase, 12" $90.00-120.00
4. Comport, 9½" $140.00-170.00
5. Basket, 7½" $100.00-130.00

Page 80, Velmoss Scroll
Row 1:
1. Vase, 5" $125.00-150.00
2. Vase, 8" $125.00-175.00
3. Bowl, 3" $75.00-100.00
Row 2:
1. Vase, 8" $125.00-150.00
2. Vase, 10" $125.00-200.00
3. Vase, 12" $200.00-250.00
4. Vase, 10" $150.00-200.00

Page 81, Rozane, 1917
Row 1:
1. Bowl, 3" $45.00-60.00
2. Comport, 8" $75.00-125.00
3. Vase, 6½" $40.00-50.00
Row 2:
1. Urn, 6½" $50.00-80.00
2. Bowl, 5" $75.00-110.00
3. Bowl, 3½" $50.00-60.00
Row 3:
1. Bowl, 5" $70.00-90.00
2. Comport, 6½" $100.00-125.00
3. Bowl, 4½" $60.00-70.00
Row 4:
1. Basket, 11" $125.00-150.00
2. Vase, 8" $65.00-90.00
3. Vase, 10" $90.00-110.00
4. Vase, 10" $90.00-110.00
5. Vase, 8" $75.00-90.00

Page 82, Azurine, Orchid and Turquoise
Bud Vase, 10", each $60.00-80.00
Console Bowl, 12" $65.00-85.00

Page 83, Lombardy; Azurine, Orchid and Turquoise
Top, left:
1. Jardiniere, 6½" $150.00-200.00
2. Vase, 6" $150.00-200.00
Center:
1. Double Bud Vase, 5" $55.00-75.00
2. Vase, 10" $125.00-150.00
3. Vase, 8" $75.00-100.00
Bottom, Row 1:
1. Vase, 6" $60.00-70.00
2. Window Box, 5" $75.00-100.00
3. Jardiniere, 4" $40.00-50.00
4. Bud Vase, 6" $50.00-60.00
Row 2:
1. Vase, 10" $75.00-100.00
2. Vase, 8" $100.00-125.00

3. Vase, 12½" $90.00-110.00

Page 84, Rosecraft Black and Colors
Row 1:
1. Comport, 4" $100.00-125.00
Row 2:
1. Bowl, 3" $50.00-75.00
2. Double Bud, 5" $60.00-75.00
3. Bowl/Frog, 2" $50.00-75.00
Row 3:
1. Bowl, 5" $45.00-50.00
2. Ginger Jar, 8" $200.00-250.00
3. Bud Vase, 8" $45.00-50.00
4. Flower Pot, 4½" $65.00-75.00
Row 4:
1. Vase, 10" $75.00-100.00
2. Vase, 13½" $140.00-180.00
3. Vase, 10" $120.00-160.00
4. Vase, 9" $125.00-150.00

Page 85, Rosecraft Vintage, Rosecraft Hexagon
Row 1:
1. Bowl, 3" $50.00-75.00
2. Vase, 6" $100.00-140.00
3. Vase, 4" $65.00-95.00
Row 2:
1. Vase, 8½" $150.00-175.00
2. Window Box, 6" $175.00-250.00
3. Vase, 12" $200.00-300.00
Bottom, Row 1:
1. Vase, 6" $125.00-150.00
2. Vase, 5" $100.00-125.00
3. Vase, 5" $100.00-125.00
4. Vase, 4" $90.00-110.00
5. Bowl, 7½" $95.00-115.00
Row 2:
1. Candlestick, 8", each $120.00-160.00
2. Vase, 8" $150.00-200.00
3. Double Bud Vase, 5" $100.00-125.00
4. Vase, 8" $150.00-200.00
5. Candlestick, 8" $120.00-160.00

Page 86, Lustre, Imperial II
Row 1:
1. Basket, 10" $100.00-150.00
2. Basket, 6" $125.00-150.00
Row 2:
1. Bowl, 5" $35.00-45.00
2. Vase, 12" $55.00-75.00
3. Candlestick, 10" $45.00-65.00
4. Candlestick, 5½' $35.00-45.00
Below:
1. Vase, 12" $100.00-150.00
2. Basket, 6½" $100.00-125.00

Page 87, Matt Color, Imperial II
Row 1:
1. Bowl, 3" $35.00-40.00
2. Vase, 4" $35.00-40.00
3. Bowl, 4" $40.00-45.00
4. Vase, 4" $30.00-35.00
5. Pot, 4" $30.00-35.00
Center:
1. Vase, 9" $150.00-200.00
2. Vase, 10" $200.00-300.00
3. Vase, 8" $175.00-225.00
4. Vase, 8" $250.00-300.00
Bottom, Row 1:
1. Bowl, 4½" $100.00-150.00
2. Vase, 5½" $75.00-100.00

3. Vase, 7" $125.00-175.00
4. Vase, 4½" $100.00-125.00
5. Pot, 6" $150.00-200.00
Row 2:
  1. Bowl, 4½" $125.00-150.00
  2. Vase, 5" $90.00-110.00
  3. Bowl, 5" $125.00-175.00
  4. Vase, 5" $125.00-175.00
Row 3:
  1. Vase, 7" $150.00-200.00
  2. Vase, 4" $70.00-90.00
  3. Bowl, 5" $150.00-200.00
  4. Vase, 7" $150.00-200.00
Row 4:
  1. Vase, 8½" $200.00-250.00
  2. Vase, 8" $175.00-200.00
  3. Vase, 11" $250.00-350.00
  4. Vase, 8½" $250.00-350.00

Page 88, Dogwood I, Dogwood II
Row 1:
  1. Vase, 7" $125.00-150.00
  2. Hanging Basket, 7" $125.00-150.00
  3. Bowl, 2½" $50.00-75.00
Row 2:
  1. Bowl, 4" $60.00-70.00
  2. Jardiniere, 6" $75.00-100.00
  3. Jardiniere, 8" $100.00-125.00
Bottom, Row 1:
  1. Double Bud, 8" $100.00-135.00
  2. Tub, 4" $80.00-100.00
Row 2:
  1. Window Box/Liner, 5½" $100.00-135.00
  2. Vase, 14½" $250.00-350.00

Page 89, Dahlrose
Row 1:
  1. Vase, 6" $90.00-110.00
  2. Hanging Basket, 7½" $150.00-175.00
  3. Pillow Vase, 5" $100.00-125.00
Row 2:
  1. Candlestick, 3½" $40.00-50.00
  2. Jardiniere, 6" $125.00-175.00
  3. Jardiniere, 4" $100.00-125.00
Row 3:
  1. Vase, 8" $125.00-175.00
  2. Window Box, 6" $150.00-200.00
  3. Bud Vase, 8" $100.00-125.00
Row 4:
  1. Window Box, 6" $175.00-225.00
  2. Window Box, 6" $150.00-200.00

Page 91, Florentine
  Hanging Basket, 9" $125.00-175.00
Row 1:
  1. Jardiniere, 5" $65.00-80.00
  2. Ashtray, 5" $50.00-60.00
  3. Vase, 8" $75.00-100.00
Row 2:
  1. Bowl, 7" $50.00-60.00
  2. Bowl, 9" $65.00-75.00
  3. Bowl, 7" $45.00-55.00
Row 3:
  1. Candlestick 10½" $100.00-125.00
  2. Candlestick, 8½" $75.00-100.00
  3. Lamp Base, 8" $150.00-200.00
  4. Vase, 7" $50.00-75.00
  5. Double Bud Vase, 4½" $50.00-75.00
Row 4:
  1. Jardiniere $150.00-200.00
  2. Window Box, 11½" $150.00-200.00

Page 92, Cremona
  1. Urn, 4" $40.00-50.00
  2. Fan, 5" $25.00-35.00
  3. Vase, 8" $50.00-65.00
  4. Vase, 12" $100.00-125.00

Page 93, Vista, Victorian Art Pottery
Row 1:
  1. Basket, 12" $275.00-325.00
  2. Vase, 10" $250.00-300.00
  3. Basket, 9½" $225.00-275.00
Row 2:
  1. Vase, 15" $400.00-500.00
  2. Vase, 18" $450.00-600.00
  3. Vase, 18" $400.00-500.00
Below, left:
  Covered Jar, 8" $300.00-400.00
Bottom, right:
Row 1:
  1. Vase, 6" $150.00-200.00
  2. Urn, 4" $125.00-150.00
Row 2:
  1. Vase, 6" $150.00-200.00
  2. Vase, 8" $200.00-300.00
  3. Vase, 7" $200.00-275.00

Page 94, Tuscany
Row 1:
  1. Vase, 4" $40.00-50.00
  2. Vase, 6" $50.00-75.00
  3. Flower Arranger, 5½" $40.00-50.00
Row 2:
  1. Vase, 6" $50.00-75.00
  2. Vase, 9" $90.00-135.00
  3. Vase, 12" $125.00-175.00

Page 95, Savona, Volpato
Row 1:
  Covered Urn, 8" $150.00-175.00
Row 2:
  1. Candlestick, 9½", pr. $175.00-200.00
  2. Vase, 12" $200.00-225.00
Bottom, Row 1:
  1. Candlestick, 3½", each $40.00-50.00
  2. Console Bowl, 4" $60.00-75.00
Row 2:
  1. Window Box, 2½" $45.00-55.00
  2. Pot/saucer, 6" $100.00-135.00
  3. Vase, 9" $125.00-150.00
  4. Candlestick, 10", each $60.00-80.00

Page 96, Normandy
  Hanging Basket, 7" $175.00-225.00

Page 97, Corinthian, La Rose
  Vase, 8½" $80.00-100.00
  Jardiniere, 7" $85.00-100.00
Center, Row 1:
  1. Wall Pocket, 8" $150.00-175.00
  2. Hanging Basket, 8" $140.00-170.00
  3. Wall Pocket, 8½" $150.00-175.00
Row 2:
  1. Footed Bowl, 4½" $60.00-70.00
  2. Vase, 6" $55.00-75.00
  3. Vase, 7" $55.00-80.00
  4. Bowl, 3" $40.00-45.00
Bottom, Row 1:
  1. Vase, 4" $60.00-80.00
  2. Bowl, 3" $50.00-65.00

Row 2:
    1. Wall Pocket, 9" $150.00-200.00
    2. Jardiniere, 6½" $75.00-110.00
    3. Vase, 6" $50.00-70.00

Page 98, Cherry Blossom, Florane
Center, left:
    Hanging Basket, 8" $400.00-500.00
Bottom:
    1. Bowl, 5" $40.00-50.00
    2. Vase, 12½" $100.00-150.00
    3. Basket, 8½" $125.00-150.00
    4. Double Bud Vase, 5" $40.00-60.00

Page 99, Russco
Row 1:
    1. Vase, 8" $80.00-110.00
    2. Vase, 7" $75.00-100.00
Row 2:
    1. Double Bud Vase, 8½" $60.00-80.00
    2. Vase, 9½" $125.00-150.00
    3. Footed Urn, 8½" $125.00-150.00
Row 3:
    1. Urn, 7" $120.00-160.00
    2. Vase, 12½" $150.00-200.00
    3. Triple Cornucopia, 8" $90.00-120.00

Page 100, Wisteria
Above, right:
    1. Vase, brown, 10" $450.00-550.00
                                     blue, $700.00-900.00
    2. Hanging Basket, 7½" $500.00-550.00
Center:
    1. Vase, 8½" $300.00-350.00
    2. Vase, 8½" $350.00-450.00
    3. Urn, 5" $250.00-350.00

Page 101, Jonquil
Row 1:
    1. Bowl, 3" $100.00-125.00
    2. Candlestick, 4" $100.00-125.00
    3. Bowl, 3½" $125.00-175.00
    4. Vase, 4½" $100.00-125.00
    5. Vase, 4" $125.00-150.00
Row 2:
    1. Urn, 4" $100.00-125.00
    2. Urn, 5½" $125.00-150.00
    3. Pot/Frog, 5½" $175.00-225.00
    4. Vase, 4½" $150.00-175.00
Row 3:
    1. Vase, 7" $150.00-200.00
    2. Vase, 6½" $160.00-200.00
    3. Vase, 6½" $150.00-200.00
    4. Crocus Pot, 7" $300.00-400.00
Row 4:
    1. Vase, 8" $150.00-200.00
    2. Vase, 9½" $175.00-225.00
    3. Vase, 12" $400.00-600.00
    4. Vase, 8" $150.00-200.00

Page 103, Futura
Row 1:
    1. Vase, 7½" $450.00-500.00
    2. Vase, 8" $450.00-500.00
    3. Vase, 7" $450.00-550.00
    4. Vase, 6" $150.00-200.00
    5. Pillow Vase, 5" $150.00-200.00
Row 2:
    1. Vase, 4" $125.00-150.00
    2. Pot, 3½" $150.00-175.00
    3. Fan Vase, 6" $175.00-200.00

    4. Pot, 4" $175.00-225.00
Row 3:
    1. Window Box, 5" $600.00-800.00
    2. Candlestick, 4" $125.00-150.00
    3. Jardiniere, 6" $175.00-225.00
Row 4:
    1. Vase, 6½" $175.00-225.00
    2. Pot, 5" $175.00-225.00
    3. Vase, 10" $450.00-600.00
    4. Vase, 8½" $500.00-600.00
    5. Vase, 7" $150.00-200.00
Bottom, right:
    1. Vase, 10", very rare $1,100.00-1,250.00
    2. Vase, 12½" $800.00-1,000.00

Page 105, Futura
Row 1:
    1. Vase, 5" $100.00-125.00
    2. Bowl, 2½" $250.00-350.00
    3. Vase, 6" $100.00-125.00
Row 2:
    1. Bowl, 3½" $150.00-200.00
    2. Bowl, 3½" $125.00-150.00
    3. Bowl, 4" $150.00-175.00
Row 3:
    1. Vase, 8" $175.00-225.00
    2. Vase, 7½" $500.00-600.00
    3. Vase, 9½" $4,000.00-5,000.00
    4. Vase, 9" $650.00-750.00
Row 4:
    1. Vase, 9" $400.00-450.00
    2. Vase, 10" $400.00-450.00
    3. Vase, 15½" $600.00-700.00
    4. Vase, 10" $450.00-550.00
    5. Vase, 8" $300.00-400.00
Bottom, Row 1:
    1. Vase, 8" $175.00-225.00
    2. Vase, 7" $450.00-550.00
    3. Vase, 9" $250.00-300.00
Row 2:
    1. Vase, 9" $450.00-550.00
    2. Vase, 10" $500.00-600.00
    3. Vase, 8" $375.00-450.00

Page 106, Laurel
    1. Vase, 10" $175.00-225.00
    2. Vase, 9½" $175.00-200.00
    3. Urn, 6½" $150.00-175.00
    4. Bowl, 3½" $100.00-125.00

Page 107, Tourmaline, Montacello
Row 1:
    1. Vase, 5½" $65.00-75.00
    2. Candlestick, 5" $40.00-50.00
    3. Pillow Vase, 6" $50.00-80.00
    4. Vase, 6" $70.00-90.00
Row 2:
    1. Urn, 4½" $65.00-90.00
    2. Vase, 7" $75.00-100.00
    3. Urn, 6" $70.00-95.00
    4. Bowl, 8" $45.00-50.00
Row 3:
    1. Cornucopia, 7" $45.00-50.00
    2. Vase, 7" $50.00-60.00
    3. Vase, 8" $75.00-90.00
    4. Vase, 7½" $60.00-75.00
    5. Urn, 5½" $50.00-60.00
Row 4:
    1. Vase, 8" $70.00-90.00
    2. Vase, 8" $70.00-100.00

3. Vase, 10" $100.00-150.00
4. Vase, 8" $80.00-100.00
5. Vase, 8" $70.00-90.00
Bottom:
1. Basket, blue, 6½" $200.00-250.00
                              brown, $250.00-300.00
2. Vase, 5" $110.00-140.00
3. Vase, 8½" $150.00-200.00
4. Vase, 10½" $250.00-325.00

Page 108, Velmoss
Top, left:
1. Vase, 14½" $150.00-225.00
2. Bowl, 11" $75.00-100.00
Center:
1. Vase, 8" $65.00-95.00
2. Vase, 12½" $125.00-175.00
3. Vase, 9½" $100.00-125.00

Page 109, Sunflower
Row 1:
1. Urn, 4" $175.00-225.00
2. Vase, 5" $200.00-250.00
3. Vase, 5" $175.00-225.00
4. Bowl, 4" $200.00-250.00
Row 2:
1. Candlestick, 4" $140.00-165.00
2. Console, 3" $275.00-325.00
Row 3:
1. Urn, 5" $275.00-325.00
2. Window Box, 3½" $350.00-450.00
3. Vase, 6" $275.00-325.00
Row 4:
1. Urn, 7" $400.00-500.00
2. Vase, 10" $550.00-650.00
3. Urn, 6" $350.00-450.00

Page 110, Pine Cone
Row 1:
1. Planter, 5" $100.00-125.00
2. Centerpiece/Candleholder, 6" $250.00-350.00
3. Bowl, 4½" $100.00-125.00
Row 2:
1. Bowl, 4½" $100.00-150.00
2. Console, 3½" $225.00-275.00
3. Ashtray, 4½" $60.00-70.00
Row 3:
1. Candlestick, 2½" $60.00-75.00
2. Mug, 4" $150.00-200.00
3. Pitcher, 9½" $400.00-500.00
4. Tumbler, 5" $150.00-200.00
5. Candlestick, 5" $100.00-150.00
Row 4:
1. Vase, 10½" $250.00-350.00
2. Vase, 14½" $500.00-600.00
3. Pitcher, 10½" $250.00-350.00

Page 111, Pine Cone
Row 1:
1. Bud Vase, 7½" $300.00-400.00
2. Pillow Vase, 8" $250.00-350.00
3. Boat Dish, 9" $200.00-250.00
Row 2:
1. Vase, 7" $100.00-140.00
2. Console, 11" $275.00-350.00
3. Vase, 7" $175.00-225.00
4. Vase, 8½" $125.00-175.00
Row 3:
1. Urn, 7" $225.00-300.00
2. Double Tray, 13" $225.00-275.00
3. Urn, 5" $200.00-250.00

Row 4:
1. Vase, 8" $125.00-150.00
2. Basket, 11" $325.00-425.00
3. Urn/Vase, 8" $175.00-225.00

Page 113, Topeo, Artcraft
Row 1:
1. Bowl, 3" $70.00-90.00
Row 2:
1. Vase, 7" $150.00-200.00
2. Bowl, 4" $175.00-250.00
3. Urn/Vase, 6" $165.00-200.00
Row 3:
1. Vase, 14" $450.00-550.00
2. Vase, 9" $150.00-200.00
3. Vase, 15" $500.00-600.00
Center, right:
Vase, 9" $300.00-400.00
Bottom, left:
Jardiniere, 4" $150.00-175.00
Bottom, right:
1. Console Bowl, 13" $100.00-150.00
2. Double Candlestick, 5" $60.00-80.00

Page 114, Luffa, Moss
Row 1:
1. Vase, 8" $175.00-225.00
2. Jardiniere, 5¼" base $250.00-350.00
3. Vase, 8½" $100.00-150.00
4. Candlestick, 5" $100.00-125.00
Row 2:
1. Lamp, 9½" $400.00-500.00
2. Vase, 15½" $500.00-600.00
3. Lamp, 9½" $400.00-500.00
Bottom:
1. Urn, 6" $125.00-150.00
2. Pillow Vase, 8" $150.00-200.00
3. Candlestick, 2", each $40.00-50.00
4. Triple Candleholder, 7" $150.00-200.00

Page 115, Clemana
Row 1:
1. Bowl, 4½" $75.00-100.00
2. Urn/Vase, 7½" $100.00-125.00
3. Flower Frog, 4" $50.00-75.00
Row 2:
1. Vase, 6½" $90.00-120.00
2. Vase, 6½" $100.00-125.00
3. Vase, 7½" $100.00-150.00
4. Vase, 6½" $90.00-120.00
Row 3:
1. Urn, 8½" $150.00-200.00
2. Vase, 12½" $250.00-300.00
3. Vase, 14" $350.00-450.00
4. Vase, 9½" $175.00-225.00

Page 116, Orian
Row 1:
1. Vase, 6" $60.00-90.00
2. Vase, 9" $100.00-125.00
3. Candleholder, 4½" $55.00-90.00
Row 2:
1. Vase, 7" $75.00-95.00
2. Console Bowl, 5 .... $100.00-150.00
3. Vase, 6½" $70.00-90.00
Page 117, Orian, Falline
Top:
1. Vase, 12½" $175.00-225.00
2. Vase, 10½" $150.00-200.00

3. Vase, 7½" $125.00-175.00
4. Comport, 4½" $70.00-90.00
Center, Row 1:
    1. Urn, 6" $225.00-275.00
    2. Vase, 6" $225.00-275.00
    3. Candleholder, 4" $125.00-150.00
    4. Bowl, 11" $125.00-150.00
Row 2:
    1. Vase, 8" $250.00-300.00
    2. Vase, 12½" $450.00-550.00
    3, Vase, 9" $300.00-350.00
    4. Vase, 7½" $225.00-275.00
Bottom, Row 1:
    1. Urn, 6" $225.00-275.00
    2. Lamp Base, 10½" $450.00-550.00
    3. Vase, 8" $300.00-350.00
Row 2:
    1. Vase, 6" $200.00-225.00
    2. Candlestick, 4½", each $175.00-200.00
    3. Bowl/Frog, 5" $250.00-300.00
    4. Vase, 4" $125.00-150.00

Page 118, Thornapple, Earlam
Row 1:
    1. Vase, 8½" $150.00-225.00
    2. Double Bud Vase, 5½" $75.00-100.00
    3. Hanging Basket, Rare 7" $300.00-400.00
    4.Triple Bud Vase, 6" $100.00-150.00
Row 2:
    1. Urn, 6½" $125.00-175.00
    2. Vase, 10½" $200.00-300.00
    3. Vase, 9" $150.00-200.00
Bottom, Row 1:
    1. Vase, 4" $70.00-80.00
    2. Vase, 6" $100.00-135.00
    3. Candlestick, 4" $125.00-175.00
Row 2:
    1. Bowl, 3" $100.00-125.00
    2. Vase, 9" $200.00-250.00
    3. Planter, 5½" $125.00-150.00

Page 119, Ixia, Windsor
    Hanging basket...$175.00-225.00
Row 1:
    1. Double Candlestick, 3" $60.00-80.00
    2. Console Bowl, 3½" $50.00-100.00
    3. Candleholder/Bud Vase $75.00-100.00
Row 2:
    1. Vase, 8½" $75.00-100.00
    2. Vase, 8½" $80.00-120.00
    3. Vase, 10½" $100.00-150.00
    4. Vase, 8½" $75.00-100.00
Bottom, Row 1:
    1. Bowl, 3½" $125.00-150.00
    2. Basket, 4½" $200.00-250.00
    3. Bowl, 3" $125.00-150.00
Row 2:
    1. Vase, 6" $125.00-150.00
    2. Vase, 7" $300.00-400.00
    3. Lamp Base, 7" $300.00-400.00

Page 120, Moderne
Row 1:
    1. Triple Candleholder, 6" $125.00-175.00
    2. Urn, 6½" $100.00-150.00
    3. Vase, 6½" $100.00-120.00
Row 2:
    1. Comport, 6" $100.00-150.00
    2. Vase, 8½" $125.00-150.00
    3. Vase, 6" $100.00-125.00
    4. Comport, 5" $100.00-125.00

Page 121, Poppy
Row 1:
    1. Jardiniere, 6½" $100.00-125.00
    2. Jardiniere, 5" $50.00-75.00
    3. Bowl, 12" $125.00-150.00
Row 2:
    1. Jardiniere, 3½" $40.00-50.00
    2. Vase, 6" $100.00-125.00
    3. Vase, 7½" $125.00-150.00
    4. Vase, 7½" $125.00-150.00
    5. Vase, 8" $150.00-175.00
Row 3:
    1. Vase, 9" $150.00-200.00
    2. Ewer, 18½" $400.00-500.00
    3. Basket, 12½" $300.00-400.00
    4. Vase, 8" $100.00-125.00

Page 122, Primrose
Top , right:
    1. Vase, 6½" $100.00-150.00
    2. Vase, 7" $100.00-150.00

Page 123, Baneda
Row 1:
    1. Bowl, 3½" $175.00-225.00
    2. Vase, 4½" $150.00-200.00
    3. Bowl, 3" $200.00-250.00
Row 2:
    1. Urn, 5" $200.00-250.00
    2. Candleholder, 5½" $150.00-175.00
    3. Urn, 7" $225.00-275.00
    4. Vase, 6" $175.00-225.00
    5. Vase, 4" $100.00-125.00
Row 3:
    1. Vase, 7" $200.00-250.00
    2. Vase, 7" $200.00-250.00
    3. Vase, 9" $250.00-325.00
    4. Vase, 8" $300.00-350.00
Row 4:
    1. Vase, 10" $325.00-375.00
    2. Vase, 12" $550.00-650.00
    3. Vase, 12" $600.00-700.00
    4. Vase, 9" $400.00-500.00

Page 124, Teasel
    1. Vase, 12" $175.00-225.00
    2. Vase, 10" $175.00-225.00
    3. Vase, 6" $60.00-80.00

Page 125, Blackberry, Morning Glory
Row 1:
    1. Vase, 6" $225.00-275.00
    2. Hanging Basket, 4½" $475.00-550.00
    3. Basket..$450.00-550.00
Row 2:
    1. Jardiniere, 7" $300.00-375.00
    2. Jardiniere, 6" $275.00-350.00
    3. Jardiniere, 4" $125.00-175.00
Bottom, Row 1:
    1. Candlestick, 5", each................................$150.00-200.00
    2. Console Bowl, 4½" $300.00-350.00
    3. Pot, 5" $200.00-250.00
Row 2:
    1. Basket, 10½" $400.00-500.00
    2. Vase, 15" $600.00-750.00
    3. Pillow Vase, 7" $225.00-275.00
Page 126, Dawn
Top, right:
    Ewer, 16" $350.00-400.00

Center:
    1. Vase, 12" $150.00-200.00
    2. Bowl, 16" $125.00-175.00

Page 127, Ivory II
    Hanging Basket, 7" $75.00-100.00
    Dog, 6½" $300.00-400.00
    Nude, 9" $400.00-500.00
Bottom, Row 1:
    1. Cornucopia, 5½" $45.00-60.00
    2. Jardiniere, 4" $40.00-50.00
    3. Urn, 6½" $55.00-75.00
Row 2:
    1. Vase, 7" $50.00-75.00
    2. Candlestick, 5½" $30.00-40.00
    3. Ewer, 10½" $50.00-75.00
    4. Candlestick, 2½" $25.00-35.00
    5. Jardiniere, 6" $45.00-50.00

Page 128, Iris
Row 1:
    1. Vase, 6½" $100.00-125.00
    2. Basket, 9½" $250.00-300.00
    3. Vase, 7½" $125.00-175.00
Row 2:
    1. Pillow Vase, 8½" $150.00-200.00
    2. Console Bowl, 3" $100.00-125.00
    3. Urn/Vase, 6½" $150.00-200.00
Row 3:
    1. Pot, 3½" $50.00-65.00
    2. Console Bowl, 3½" $125.00-175.00
    3. Vase, 5" $50.00-60.00
Row 4:
    1. Vase, 8" $125.00-150.00
    2. Vase, 12½" $225.00-325.00
    3. Vase, 10" $175.00-250.00

Page 129, Bleeding Heart
    Hanging Basket, 8" $175.00-225.00
Row 1:
    1. Pot, 3½" $35.00-50.00
    2. Vase, 8" $100.00-150.00
    3. Bowl, 4" $50.00-75.00
    4. Vase, 8½" $100.00-150.00
    5. Vase, 6½" $100.00-125.00
Row 2:
    1. Candlestick, 5" $65.00-90.00
    2. Console/Frog, 17", set $200.00-250.00
Row 3:
    1. Basket, 9½" $150.00-200.00
    2. Vase, 15" $300.00-400.00
    3. Plate, 10½" $100.00-150.00

Page 130, Columbine
Row 1:
    1. Vase, 7½" $100.00-135.00
    2. Hanging Basket, 8½" $150.00-200.00
    3. Vase, 8" $100.00-140.00
Row 2:
    1. Bookend/Planter, 5", each $125.00-175.00
    2. Candleholder, 5", each $60.00-80.00
    3. Cornucopia, 5½" $45.00-60.00

Page 131, Fuchsia
Row 1:
    1. Vase, 6" $125.00-150.00
    2. Vase, 6" $125.00-150.00
    3. Vase, 6" $125.00-150.00
Row 2:
    1. Candlestick, 2", each $60.00-70.00
    2. Console Bowl, 3½" $125.00-175.00

Row 3:
    1. Candlestick, 5½", each $125.00-150.00
    2. Console Bowl/Frog, 4", 2 piece $200.00-250.00
Row 4:
    1. Vase, 8" $175.00-225.00
    2. Vase, 8½" $175.00-225.00
    3. Vase, 8" $175.00-225.00

Page 132, Cosmos
    Hanging Basket, 7" $200.00-250.00
Row 1:
    1. Vase, 8" $125.00-150.00
    2. Vase, 5" $50.00-75.00
    3. Urn, 4" $75.00-110.00
    4. Vase, 6½" $75.00-95.00
    5. Vase, 12½" $225.00-325.00
Row 2:
    1. Vase, 4" $40.00-50.00
    2. Console Bowl, 15½" $150.00-200.00
    3. Flower Frog, 3½" $50.00-75.00

Page 133, White Rose
Row 1:
    1. Vase, 4" $40.00-50.00
    2. Vase, 5" $60.00-75.00
    3. Basket, 7½" $150.00-200.00
    4. Vase, 6" $75.00-95.00
    5. Candlestick, 4½" $50.00-70.00
Row 2:
    1. Urn, 7" $150.00-200.00
    2. Vase, 8" $125.00-150.00
    3. Vase, 8½" $150.00-200.00
Row 3:
    1. Double Bud Vase, 4½" $70.00-90.00
    2. Console/Frog, 16½" $125.00-200.00
    3. Double Candleholder, 4", each $90.00-120.00
Row 4:
    1. Vase, 12½" $225.00-300.00
    2. Vase, 15½" $300.00-400.00
    3. Vase, 9" $150.00-200.00

Page 134, Bittersweet
Row 1:
    1. Basket, 8½" $75.00-110.00
    2. Vase, 6" $40.00-50.00
    3. Urn, 7" $80.00-100.00
Row 2:
    1. Planter, 10½" $75.00-100.00
    2. Planter, 11½" $75.00-100.00
    3. Cornucopia, 4½" $40.00-50.00
Row 3:
    1. Candlestick, 3" $40.00-50.00
    2. Console Bowl, 12½" $100.00-125.00
    3. Same as #1
    4. Double Vase, 4" $55.00-80.00
Row 4:
    1. Vase, 7" $65.00-85.00
    2. Vase, 10" $100.00-130.00
    3. Vase, 15½" $250.00-350.00
    4. Vase, 8" $90.00-110.00

Page 135, Foxglove
Row 1:
    1. Tray, 8½" $75.00-90.00
    2. Hanging Basket, 6½" $200.00-250.00
    3. Cornucopia, 6" $60.00-85.00
Row 2:
    1. Tray, 15" $90.00-125.00
    2. Flower Frog, 4" $50.00-75.00
    3. Tray, 11" $75.00-100.00

Row 3:
1. Vase, 12½" $250.00-350.00
2. Vase, 14" $300.00-400.00
3. Vase, 10" $175.00-225.00
4. Vase, 8½" $125.00-175.00

Page 136, Peony
Row 1:
1. Bookend, 5½", pr..$150.00-200.00
2. Conch Shell, 9½" $75.00-100.00
3. Tray, 8"...$40.00-55.00
Row 2:
1. Planter, 10" $60.00-85.00
2. Bowl, 11"..$80.00-100.00
Row 3:
1. Double Candleholder, 5"..............................$45.00-65.00
2. Mug, 3½"..$75.00-100.00
3. Pitcher, 7½"..$150.00-200.00
4. Frog, 4"...$40.00-50.00
Row 4:
1. Vase, 8" $75.00-90.00
2. Basket, 11"..$200.00-250.00
3. Vase, 14" $225.00-275.00

Page 137, Magnolia
Row 1:
1. Planter, 8½"..$60.00-90.00
2. Planter, 6" $60.00-85.00
3. Candlestick, 5"..$60.00-85.00
4. Candlestick, 2½" $40.00-50.00
Row 2:
1. Ashtray, 7" $60.00-80.00
2. Console Bowl, 14½"...$125.00-175.00
3. Cornucopia, 6" $50.00-75.00
Row 3:
1. Vase, 6" $75.00-95.00
2. Flower Frog, 5½"...$40.00-60.00
3. Conch Shell, 6½" $50.00-75.00
4. Vase, 6" $50.00-75.00
Row 4:
1. Basket, 12"..$125.00-175.00
2. Ewer, 10" $100.00-125.00
3. Vase, 8" $100.00-135.00

Page 138, Water Lily
1. Vase, 9" $125.00-150.00
2. Candlestick, 5"..$65.00-90.00
3. Hanging Basket, 9"...$175.00-225.00
4. Frog, 4½" $40.00-55.00

Page 139, Freesia
Row 1:
1. Flower Pot/Saucer, 5½"..................................$85.00-110.00
2. Basket, 7" $90.00-120.00
3. Bowl, 4"..$60.00-75.00
Row 2:
1. Bowl, 8½" $60.00-70.00
2. Bowl, 11"..$100.00-135.00
Row 3:
1. Candlestick, 2", each $40.00-50.00
2. Console, 16½"...$125.00-150.00
Row 4:
1. Urn/Vase, 5"..$70.00-95.00
2. Vase, 7" $80.00-100.00
3. Window Box, 10½"..$75.00-100.00
Row 5:
1. Vase, 8" $75.00-100.00
2. Vase, 9½" $90.00-120.00
3. Vase, 10½" $125.00-160.00
4. Vase, 9" $100.00-150.00

Page 140, Rozane Pattern
1. Vase, 12" $90.00-120.00
2. Bowl, 7½", set $100.00-150.00
3. Vase, 8½" $75.00-100.00

Page 141, Zephyr Lily
Row 1:
1. Fan Vase, 6" $65.00-90.00
2. Hanging Basket, 7½" $150.00-175.00
3. Pillow Vase, 7" $75.00-100.00
Row 2:
1. Candlestick, 2" $40.00-50.00
2. Console Bowl, 16½"..$125.00-175.00
3. Bud Vase, 7½" $50.00-80.00
Row 3:
1. Vase, 8½" $70.00-100.00
2. Tray, 14½" $100.00-135.00
3. Cornucopia, 8½" $60.00-70.00
Row 4:
1. Vase, 9½" $80.00-100.00
2. Vase, 12" $135.00-160.00
3. Vase, 12½" $135.00-170.00
4. Urn Vase, 8½" $100.00-135.00

Page 142, Clematis
Row 1:
1. Console Bowl, 14" $100.00-125.00
2. Candleholder, 2½"..$35.00-40.00
3. Console Bowl, 9" $50.00-70.00
Row 2:
1. Flower Arranger, 5½" $40.00-50.00
2. Flower Pot, 5½" $80.00-110.00
3. Vase, 6" $40.00-50.00
4. Flower Frog, 4½" $35.00-40.00
5. Vase, 6½" $40.00-50.00

Page 143, Snowberry
Row 1:
1. Urn, 6" $75.00-100.00
2. Pillow Vase, 6½" $60.00-75.00
3. Flower Pot, 5½" $90.00-120.00
Row 2:
1. Candlestick, 4½", each $50.00-75.00
2. Console Bowl, 11"..$50.00-75.00
Row 3:
1. Vase, 6" $50.00-60.00
2. Tray, 14" $90.00-125.00
3. Vase, 7½" $60.00-70.00
Row 4:
1. Vase, 12½" $100.00-150.00
2. Ewer, 16" $225.00-275.00
3. Basket, 12½"..$125.00-175.00
4. Vase, 8½" $100.00-120.00

Page 144, Apple Blossom
Row 1:
1. Bowl, 2½" $60.00-80.00
2. Jardiniere, 6" $100.00-135.00
3. Window Box, 2½" $50.00-70.00
Row 2:
1. Vase, 10" $135.00-185.00
2. Vase, 15½" $300.00-425.00
3. Vase, 12½" $200.00-250.00

Page 145, Gardenia
Hanging Basket, 6"...$150.00-175.00
Row 1:
1. Bowl, 5"..$55.00-75.00
2. Window Box, 3" $50.00-70.00
3. Vase, 8"...$75.00-100.00

Row 2:
    1. Vase, 10" $100.00-135.00
    2. Tray, 15" $90.00-125.00
    3. Vase, 10½" $110.00-140.00
Row 3:
    1. Basket, 12" $140.00-190.00
    2. Vase, 12" $130.00-170.00
    3. Vase, 14½" $100.00-275.00

Page 146, Mayfair
Row 1:
    1. Jardiniere, 7½" $30.00-35.00
    2. Pitcher, 5" $35.00-40.00
    3. Pitcher, 5" $35.00-40.00
    4. Cornucopia, 3" $30.00-35.00
Bottom, Row 1:
    1. Jardiniere, 4" $25.00-30.00
    2. Planter, 3½" $30.00-35.00
Row 2:
    1. Pot, 4½" $35.00-40.00
    2. Vase, 7" $45.00-50.00
    3. Pot, 5" $40.00-45.00
Row 3:
    1. Candlestick, 4½" $15.00-20.00
    2. Bowl, 7" $25.00-30.00
    3. Bowl, 10" $40.00-45.00
    4. Vase, 12½" $60.00-70.00

Page 147, Bushberry
Row 1:
    1. Double Cornucopia, 6" $90.00-110.00
    2. Candlestick, 2", each $60.00-70.00
    3. Hanging Basket, 7" $325.00-375.00
    4. Vase, 4" $50.00-70.00
    5. Vase, 7" $70.00-100.00
Row 2:
    1. Double Bud Vase, 4½" $90.00-110.00
    2. Console Bowl, 13" $125.00-175.00
    3. Planter, 6½" $90.00-110.00
Row 3:
    1. Cider Pitcher, 8½" $250.00-325.00
    2. Mug, 3½" $100.00-135.00
    3. Vase, 6" $75.00-90.00
    4. Bud Vase, 7½" $75.00-125.00
    5. Urn, 6" $100.00-135.00
Row 4:
    1. Vase, 8" $100.00-125.00
    2. Vase, 12½" $225.00-275.00
    3. Vase, 14½" $300.00-400.00
    4. Vase, 8" $100.00-125.00

Page 148, Florane, late line
Left, Row 1:
    1. Bowl, 10" $30.00-35.00
    2. Bowl, 9" $35.00-40.00
Row 2:
    1. Bowl, 6" $20.00-25.00
    2. Bowl, 12" $45.00-50.00
    3. Bowl, 8" $20.00-25.00
Row 3:
    1. Vase, 6" $30.00-35.00
    2. Bud Vase, 7" $30.00-35.00
    3. Vase, 7" $30.00-35.00
Row 4:
    1. Vase, 9" $75.00-90.00
    2. Vase, 11" $75.00-100.00
    3. Vase, 14" $90.00-115.00
Right, Row 1:
    1. Planter Box, 6" $25.00-30.00
    2. Bowl, 7" $20.00-25.00
    3. Planter, 6" $25.00-30.00
Row 2:
    1. Planter, 10" $45.00-50.00

    2. Planter, 4" $20.00-25.00
    3. Planter, 8" $35.00-40.00
Row 3:
    1. Pot, 4" $20.00-25.00
    2. Pot, 5" $25.00-30.00
    3. Pot, 6" $35.00-40.00
    4. Bowl, 10" $25.00-30.00
Row 4:
    1. Sand Jar, 12" $100.00-135.00
    2. Jar, 10" $100.00-125.00
    3. Jar, 8" $90.00-115.00

Page 149, Wincraft
Row 1:
    1. Cornucopia, 9" $50.00-60.00
    2. Dealer Sign $600.00-800.00
    3. Mug, 4½" $50.00-60.00
Row 2:
    1. Bowl, 4" $50.00-80.00
    2. Bookends, 6½" $90.00-125.00
Row 3:
    1. Vase, 16" $135.00-185.00
    2. Ewer, 19" $200.00-250.00
Bottom, right:
    1. Vase, 7" $75.00-90.00
    2. Basket, 12" $100.00-150.00

Page 150, Artwood
Row 1:
    1. 3-pc. set $80.00-100.00
    2. Planter, 6½" $50.00-70.00
Row 2:
    1. Planter, 7" $50.00-70.00
    2. Vase, 8" $55.00-75.00

    3. Planter, 6½" $50.00-70.00

Page 151, Ming Tree
    Hanging Basket, 6" $150.00-200.00
Row 1:
    1. Bowl, 4" $45.00-50.00
    2. Planter, 4" $40.00-45.00
    3. Window Box $75.00-90.00
Row 2:
    1. Bookend, 5½", pr. $100.00-150.00
    2. Vase, 6½" $70.00-90.00
    3. Ashtray, 6" $40.00-50.00
    4. Conch Shell, 8½" $40.00-50.00
    5. Vase, 10½" $125.00-175.00
Row 3:
    1. Vase, 12½" $135.00-200.00
    2. Vase, 14½" $275.00-375.00
    3. Basket, 14½" $175.00-225.00
    4. Basket, 13" $200.00-250.00

Page 153, Raymor
Row 1:
    1. Gravy, 9½" $25.00-35.00
    2. Salad Bowl, 11½" $25.00-40.00
    3. Glass Tumblers, 4½", each $35.00-55.00
Row 2:
    1. Individual Casserole, 7½" $30.00-40.00
    2. Individual Corn Server, 12½" $20.00-25.00
    3. Shirred Egg, 10" $25.00-35.00
Row 3:
    1. Individual Covered Ramekin, 6½" $30.00-45.00
    2. Divided Vegetable Bowl, 13" $35.00-55.00
    3. Covered Butter, 7½" $75.00-100.00
Row 4:
    1. Handled Coffee Tumbler, 4" $40.00-50.00

2. Condiment Set:
Tray..$30.00-50.00
Cruet..$50.00-75.00
   Mustard..$50.00-75.00
   Salt and Pepper..$50.00-75.00
3. Large Casserole, 13½"....................................$60.00-90.00
Add $25.00 for lid

Row 5:
1. Vegetable, 9" $30.00-40.00
2. Water Pitcher..$100.00-150.00
3. Meduim Casserole, 11"....................................$50.00-80.00

Page 154, Silhouette, Lotus
Row 1:
1. Box, 4½" $40.00-50.00
2. Double Planter, 5½" $60.00-75.00
3. Ewer, 6½"..$40.00-45.00
Row 2:
1. Vase, 6" $40.00-55.00
2. Vase, 8" $50.00-70.00
3. Vase, 14"...$175.00-250.00
4. Vase, 10"...$300.00-400.00
5. Vase, 6" $40.00-55.00
Bottom:
1. Planter, 3½" $50.00-60.00
2. Pillow Vase, 10½"...$100.00-150.00
3. Bowl, 3"..$60.00-70.00

Page 155, Raymor Modern Artware, Utility Line
Row 1:
1. Vase, 6½" $95.00-115.00
2. Bowl, 3"..$65.00-75.00
Row 2:
1. Ashtray, 3½" $25.00-35.00
2. Leaf, 10" $25.00-30.00
3. Square Dish, 4"..$25.00-35.00
4. Same as #1
Row 3:
1. Wall Pocket, 10½" $125.00-175.00
2. Vase, 12½" $75.00-125.00
3. Star, 2" $45.00-50.00
Row 4:
1. Teapot, 6½" $50.00-65.00
2. Cookie Jar, 10"...$110.00-175.00
3. Mixing Bowl, 5½"..$35.00-40.00
Bottom:
1. Bowl, 9"..$45.00-60.00
2. Bowl, 8"..$40.00-45.00
3. Bowl, 7"..$35.00-40.00

Page 156, Mock Orange
Row 1:
1. Window Box, 8½"..$40.00-50.00
2. Planter, 3½"...$35.00-45.00
3. Planter, 4" $40.00-55.00
Row 2:
1. Vase, 8½" $45.00-50.00
2. Vase, 13"...$100.00-135.00
3. Pillow Vase, 7" $45.00-60.00

Page 157, Capri
1. Basket, 9" $70.00-95.00
2. Ashtray, 13"..$35.00-40.00
Bottom, Row 1:
1. Leaf, 16" $25.00-35.00
2. Leaf, 15" $25.00-35.00
Row 2:
1. Window Box, 3" $35.00-45.00
2. Planter, 5" $45.00-50.00
Row 3:
1. Bowl, 9"..$20.00-25.00

2. Ashtray, 9" $30.00-35.00
3. Bowl, 7" $20.00-25.00
Row 4:
1. Planter, 7" $50.00-65.00
2. Shell, 13½"...$40.00-45.00
3. Vase, 9" $45.00-50.00

Page 158
Row 1:
1. Leaf Dish, 10½" $25.00-30.00
2. Basket, 7" $70.00-90.00
Row 2:
1. Bowl, 7" $20.00-25.00
2. Cornucopia, 6" $40.00-45.00
3. Bowl, 7" $20.00-25.00
Row 3:
1. Ashtray, 8½" $20.00-25.00
2. Candlestick, 3"...$15.00-20.00
3. Planter, 10" $30.00-35.00
Row 4:
1. Ashtray, 13" $30.00-35.00
2. Ashtray, 13" $30.00-35.00

Page 159, Pasadena
Row 1:
1. Ashtray, 8½" $25.00-30.00
2. Ashtray, 5½" $15.00-20.00
3. Ashtray $25.00-30.00
Row 2:
1. Tray, 8" $25.00-30.00
2. Planter, 4" $25.00-30.00
3. Section of relish $15.00-20.00
Row 3:
1. Planter, 9" $30.00-35.00
2. Planter, 6½" $30.00-35.00
3. Planter, 3½" $35.00-40.00
Add $5.00 for Brass Frame
Bottom, Row 1:
1. Bowl, 2"..$15.00-20.00
2. Skillet, 6½" $25.00-30.00
3. Pot $20.00-25.00
Row 2:
1. Bowl $25.00-30.00
2. Skillet $35.00-40.00
Pot in blue $30.00-35.00
3. Box $50.00-75.00

Page 160, Wall Pockets
Row 1:
1. Chloron Boy..$600.00-800.00
2. Chloron Corner Vase $550.00-650.00
3. Chloron Girl $600.00-800.00
Row 2:
1. Chloron, 11½"...$250.00-350.00
2. Chloron Sconce, 12½" $700.00-900.00
3. Chloron, 11"...$250.00-350.00
Row 3:
1. Antique Matt Green, 10" $200.00-250.00
2. Matt Green, 11"..$225.00-275.00

Page 161, Wall Pockets, Sconces
Row 1:
1. Chloron Sconce, 17"...$750.00-950.00
2. Chloron Sconce, 12"...$550.00-750.00
3. Chloron Sconce, 17"..$800.00-1,000.00
Row 2:
1. Matt Green, 15" $225.00-275.00
2. Chloron Letter Receiver, 15½"..............................$500.00-600.00
3. Chloron Sconce, 10"..$350.00-450.00
Row 3:
1. Chloron/Nude, 8½"...$600.00-800.00
2. Chloron, 8"...$550.00-750.00

Page 162, Wall Pockets
Top Center:
    Landscape, 2½" $200.00-250.00
Row 1:
    1. Persian, 11" $250.00-300.00
    2. Ceramic Design, 17" $400.00-500.00
    3. Ceramic Design, 10" $200.00-250.00
Row 2:
    1. Pink Tint, 14½" $200.00-250.00
    2. Persian, 13½" $350.00-400.00
    3. Green Tint, 14½" $200.00-250.00
Row 3:
    1. Yellow Tint, 10" $125.00-150.00
    2. Ceramic Design, 11" $200.00-250.00
    3. Ivory I, 10" $150.00-200.00
    4. Green Tint, 10" $100.00-150.00

Page 163, Wall Pockets
Row 1:
    1. Carnelian I, 9½" $100.00-135.00
    2. Carnelian I, 8" $100.00-125.00
    3. Carnelian I, 8" $100.00-125.00
    4. Carnelian I, 8" $100.00-125.00
Row 2:
    1. Carnelian II, 8" $125.00-150.00
    2. Carnelian II, 8" $125.00-150.00
    3. Carnelian II, 8" $125.00-150.00
    4. Carnelian II, 8" $125.00-150.00
Row 3:
    1. Azurine, Orchid and Turquoise, 10" $150.00-175.00
    2. Rosecraft Blue, 10½" $150.00-175.00
    3. Rosecraft Black, 9" $150.00-175.00
    4. Rosecraft Yellow, 10" $150.00-175.00
Row 4:
    1. Mostique, 9½" $150.00-175.00
    2. Volpato, 8½" $225.00-275.00
    3. Velmos Scroll, 11" $175.00-225.00
    4. Rozane 1917, 7½" $125.00-150.00

Page 164, Wall Pockets
Row 1:
    1. Dogwood II, 9"..$125.00-175.00
    2. Dogwood II, 15"..$400.00-500.00
    3. Donatello, 11½" $125.00-150.00
    4. Donatello, 9" $100.00-125.00
Row 2:
    1. Corinthian, 12" $150.00-200.00
    2. Vista, 9½" $325.00-450.00
    3. Ivory Florentine, 8½" $110.00-135.00
    4. Florentine, 12½" $150.00-175.00
Row 3:
    1. Savona, 8" $250.00-300.00
    2. Imperial I, 10" $100.00-150.00
    3. Imperial I, 10" $100.00-150.00
    4. Dogwood I, 9½" $125.00-150.00
Row 4:
    1. Lombardy, 8" $175.00-225.00
    2. Lombardy, 8" $175.00-225.00
    3. Rosecraft Vintage, 9" $125.00-175.00
    4. Rosecraft Vintage, 9" $125.00-175.00

Page 165, Wall Pockets
Row 1:
    1. Florane, 9" $90.00-125.00
    2. Florane, 10½" $110.00-135.00
    3. Rosecraft Hexagon, 8½" $150.00-250.00
    4. La Rose, 12" $200.00-275.00
    5. La Rose, 7½" $110.00-145.00
Row 2:
    1. Futura, 8" $250.00-300.00
    2. Tuscany, 7" $120.00-150.00

    3. Rosecraft Hexagon, 8½" $150.00-250.00
    4. Tuscany, 7" $120.00-150.00
    5. Earlam, 6½" $200.00-250.00
Row 3:
    1. Imperial II, 6½" $225.00-275.00
    2. Imperial II, 6½" $250.00-300.00
    3. Imperial II, 6½" $250.00-325.00
    4. Imperial II, 6½" $275.00-350.00
Row 4:
    1. Dahlrose, 10" $150.00-200.00
    2. Panel, 7" $300.00-400.00
    3. Panel, 9" $125.00-175.00
    4. Panel, 9" $125.00-200.00

Page 166, Wall Pockets
Row 1:
    1. Blackberry, 8½" $500.00-750.00
    2. Sunflower, 7½" $500.00-650.00
    3. Wisteria, 8" $550.00-650.00
Row 2:
    1. Velmoss, 8½" $400.00-500.00
    2. Ferella, 6½" $550.00-750.00
    3. Baneda, 8" $1,000.00-1,400.00
    4. Jonquil, 8½" $300.00-400.00
    5. Morning Glory, 8½" $550.00-700.00
Row 3:
    1. Cherry Blossom, 8" $500.00-600.00
    2. Thornapple, 8½" $450.00-650.00
    3. Moss, 10" $450.00-650.00
    4. Luffa, 8½" $450.00-550.00
Row 4:
    1. Thornapple, 8" $350.00-450.00
    2. Orian, 8" $300.00-400.00
    3. Moss, 8" $250.00-400.00

Page 167, Wall Pockets, Royal Capri
Row 1:
    1. Peony, 8" $150.00-200.00
    2. Iris, 8" $250.00-350.00
    3. Fuschia, 8½" $350.00-450.00
    4. Bleeding Heart, 8½" $250.00-350.00
Row 2:
    1. Primrose, 8½" $400.00-500.00
    2. Poppy, 8½" $275.00-375.00
    3. Cosmos, 8½" $275.00-350.00
Row 3:
    1. Pine Cone, 8½" ....Brown $275.00-325.00
                                            Blue $250.00-350.00
                                        Green $125.00-175.00
    2. Pine Cone Plate, 7½" $250.00-350.00
    3. Pine Cone, 9"...$450.00-650.00
Row 4:
    1. Pine Cone Wall Shelf.......................................$250.00-350.00
    2. Pine Cone, 8½" $225.00-325.00
    3. Ivory II, 8½" $125.00-175.00
    4. Ivory II, Shelf, 5½" $100.00-135.00
Bottom, left:
    1. Leaf, 2" $200.00-225.00
    2. Vase, 9" $250.00-275.00
Bottom, right:
    Wall Pocket, 5" $300.00-400.00

Page 168, Wall Pockets
Row 1:
    1. Florentine, 7" $100.00-150.00
    2. Florentine, 9½" $125.00-175.00
    3. Dahlrose, 9" $125.00-175.00
    4. Imperial I, 8" $125.00-150.00
Row 2, center:
    Wincraft, 5" $130.00-180.00

Row 3:
1. Dogwood II, 10"..$150.00-200.00
2. Carnelian II, 7"..$125.00-150.00
3. Tuscany, 8"...$125.00-150.00
4. Velmoss Scroll, 11½"...$200.00-300.00
Row 4:
1. Chloron, 10½"..$300.00-400.00
2. Mayfair, 8"..$90.00-120.00
3. Mostique, 10½"...$100.00-150.00
Row 5:
1. White Rose, 6½"..$150.00-200.00
2. Capri, 5"...$150.00-200.00
3. Lotus, 7½"..$150.00-225.00
4. Wincraft, 8½"...$100.00-150.00
5. Cosmos, 6½"...$125.00-175.00

Page 169, Wall Pockets
Row 1:
1. Gardenia, 9½"..$125.00-175.00
2. Foxglove, 8"..$175.00-225.00
3. Columbine, 8½"..$200.00-275.00
4. Freesia, 8½"..$115.00-150.00
Row 2:
1. Apple Blossom, 8½"...$135.00-175.00
2. Zephyr Lily, 8"...$120.00-155.00
3. Magnolia, 8½"..$115.00-145.00
4. Bittersweet, 7½"..$90.00-120.00
Row 3:
1. White Rose, 8½"...$225.00-275.00
2. Snowberry, 8"...$125.00-150.00
3. Clematis, 8½"...$100.00-135.00
4. Bushberry, 8"...$200.00-300.00
blue, $300.00-400.00
Row 4:
1. Silhouette, 8"...$125.00-165.00
2. Burmese, 7½"..$175.00-250.00
3. Burmese, 7½"..$175.00-225.00
4. Ming Tree, 8½"..$150.00-200.00

Page 170, Experimentals
All are valued at $450.00-550.00 each.

Page 171, Experimentals
1. Pine Cone Design, 6"...$300.00-400.00
2. Pine Cone Design, 8"...$300.00-400.00
3. Vase, 5"...$300.00-350.00
Row 2:
1. Nude, 10"...$600.00-700.00
2. Nude, 10"...$600.00-700.00
3. Nude, 10"...$600.00-700.00
Row 3:
1. Nude, 12½"...$650.00-850.00
2. Pine Cone Design, 20½"...$800.00-1,000.00
3. Dogwood Design, 16½"...$450.00-650.00
Bottom:
1. Serra, 6"..$175.00-225.00
2. Pine Cone, 9"...$250.00-300.00
3. Vase, 9"...$450.00-550.00
4. Mock Orange, 8"...$100.00-150.00
5. Decorated Imperial II, 5"..$250.00-300.00

Page 172, Experimentals, Trial Glazes
Row 1:
1. Primrose Design, 10"..$450.00-550.00
2. Sweet Syrinca, 8½"..$450.00-550.00
3. Vase, 8"...$450.00-550.00
4. Vase, 10"...$450.00-550.00
Row 2:
1. Gladiola Design, 9½"..$450.00-550.00
2. Bittersweet Vase, 13"..$500.00-600.00

3. Arrowhead Design, 13"..$500.00-600.00
4. Freesia Design, 8½"...$400.00-450.00
Bottom, Row 1:
Plates, 8", each..$175.00-225.00
Row 2:
1. Planter, 3"..$100.00-150.00
2. Ming Tree, 8"...$200.00-300.00
3. Window Box, 3½"...$125.00-175.00
Row 3:
1. Laurel, 8"...$450.00-550.00
2. Wild Rose, 10"..$350.00-450.00
3. Vase, 8½"...$400.00-475.00
4. Moderne, 8"...$175.00-250.00

Page 173, Trials, Experimentals
Row 1:
1. Tulip Vase, 6"...$200.00-300.00
2. Savona, 6"..$200.00-300.00
3. Baneda, 6"...$200.00-300.00
4. Vase, 7"...$150.00-200.00
5. Cherry Blossom Bowl, 4".......................................$175.00-250.00
Row 2:
1. Morning Glory, 8"..$800.00-1,100.00
2. Morning Glory...$800.00-900.00
3. Morning Glory...$800.00-1,000.00
Row 3:
1. Cherry Blossom, 7"..$600.00-900.00
2. Cosmos, 8"...$650.00-800.00
3. Freesia Design, 7"...$450.00-550.00
4. Stylized Honeysuckle, 6½"......................................$400.00-450.00
Row 4:
1. Floral Design, 8"...$500.00-600.00
2. Wild Grape Design, 9½"...$700.00-900.00
3. Cherry Blossom Design, 7".....................................$500.00-550.00
Bottom:
Plates, each..$250.00-450.00

Page 174, Umbrella Stands, Lamps
Top:
1. #727 blended, 20"...$250.00-350.00
2. Earlam, 20"..$400.00-500.00
3. #609 Blended, 20"..$275.00-350.00
Bottom:
1. Base, 11½"...$225.00-325.00
2. Imperial II, 5"...$300.00-400.00
3. Base, 12"...$250.00-350.00
4. Base, 8½"...$220.00-275.00

Page 175, Lamps, Radiator Cover
Row 1:
1. Base, 8"...$300.00-400.00
2. Base, 8"...$300.00-400.00
Row 2:
1. Base, 7"...$225.00-275.00
2. Base, 10"...$450.00-550.00
3. Base, 7½"...$400.00-500.00
Row 3:
1. Base, 8½"...$150.00-200.00
2. Base, 10½"...$450.00-550.00
3. Base, 5½"...$175.00-250.00
Bottom:
Radiator Cover, set made exclusively for Russell T. Young

Page 176, Umbrella Stands
Top:
1. Blended Basketweave, 21".....................................$250.00-350.00
2. #701 blended, 22"...$250.00-325.00
3. #734 Blended, 21"..$200.00-225.00
Bottom:
1. #132 Blended, 21½"...$300.00-400.00

2. Blended Stork, 19".................................$300.00-375.00
3. #719 Blended 22".................................$300.00-400.00

Page 177, Jardinieres and Pedestals
Top:
1. Blended, 29½"....................................$400.00-500.00
2. Matt Green, 36".................................$950.00-1,250.00
3. Decorated Creamware, 29" $600.00-750.00
Bottom:
1. Ivory Florentine, 29".............................$700.00-850.00
2. Ivory Cameo, 34"................................$600.00-700.00
3. Rozane, 1917, 28½" $500.00-650.00

Page 178, Jardinieres and Pedestals
Top:
1. Decorated Landscape, 43" $3,000.00-4,000.00
2. Umbrella Stand, 22"......................$1,750.00-2,250.00
3. Decorated Landscape, 44" $3,000.00-4,000.00
Bottom:
1. Blended Iris, 31" $500.00-600.00
2. #441 Blended, 38" $600.00-800.00
3. #414 Blended, 28" $400.00-600.00

Page 179, Jardinieres and Pedestals, Umbrella Stands
Top:
1. Ceramic, 49"...............................$1,500.00-1,700.00
2. Fleur De Lis, 20½" $400.00-450.00
Bottom:
1. Gold and Silver Decorated, 22½".........$900.00-1,200.00
2. Decorated Matte, 20"....................$2,500.00-3,000.00
3. Gold and Silver Decorated, 21½".........$900.00-1,100.00

Page 180, Umbrella Stands, Jardinieres and Pedestals
Top:
1. Normandy, 20" $600.00-700.00
2. Tourist, 22½" $2,500.00-3,500.00
3. Corinthian, 20".....................................$400.00-500.00
Center:
1. Donatello, 34" $1,000.00-1,250.00
2. Rosecraft Vintage, 30½" $750.00-1,000.00
3. Corinthian, 30½"..................................$500.00-600.00
Bottom:
1. Ivory II, Sand Jar, 14½" $250.00-300.00
2. Ivory Florentine Urn, 16½" $325.00-400.00
3. Ivory Florentine Umbrella, 18½"............$250.00-350.00
4. Normandy Sand Jar, 14"........................$350.00-400.00

Page 181, Jardinieres and Pedestals, Rozane Floor Vases
Top:
1. Decorated Creamware, 26" $500.00-600.00
2. Rozane, 28"...................................$750.00-1,000.00
3. Florentine, 25" $675.00-850.00
4. Wisteria, 24½"...............................$1,500.00-2,000.00
Wisteria blue, $2,500-3,000.00

Bottom:
1. Vase, 25" $1,500.00-2,000.00
2. Vase, 29½" $2,000.00-3,000.00
3. Vase, 20" $1,750.00-2,250.00

Page 182, Jardinieres and Pedestals
Top:
1. Donatello, 23½"...................................$500.00-600.00
2. Artcraft, 24½" $750.00-950.00
3. Cherry Blossom, 25½" $1,500.00-2,000.00
4. Corinthian, 24"....................................$450.00-550.00
Bottom:
1. Artcraft, 28"..$750.00-950.00
2. Blackberry, 8"................................$2,900.00-3,200.00
3. Dahlrose, 30½" $750.00-900.00

Page 183, Jardinieres and Pedestals
Top:
1. Dogwood I, 30"....................................$650.00-750.00
2. Rozane, 1917, 35"................................$450.00-600.00
3. Vista, 28" $1,250.00-1,500.00
Bottom:
1. Jonquil, 29" $1,250.00-1,600.00
2. Normandy, 28" $800.00-900.00
3. Sunflower, 29"...............................$2,000.00-3,000.00

Page 184, Jardinieres and Pedestals, Umbrella Stands, Birdbath
Top:
1. Matt Green, 23" $350.00-450.00
2. Peony, 30" $600.00-800.00
3. Blended Mostique, 27½" $250.00-350.00
Bottom, left:
Birdbath/Planter, 30"...............................$300.00-400.00
Bottom, right:
1. Foxglove, 30½" $800.00-1,000.00
2. Rosecraft Blended, 28".........................$600.00-800.00

Page 185
Top: Jardinieres and Pedestals, Umbrella Stands and Floor Vases
1. Snowberry, 25".....................................$575.00-750.00
2. Luffa, 24½" $750.00-1,150.00
3. LaRose, 24½" $650.00-850.00
4. Zephyr Lily, 25" $675.00-825.00
Center:
1. Earlam, 12½" $300.00-450.00
2. Carnelian, I, 18½" $500.00-600.00
3. Ming Tree, 15½" $550.00-650.00
4. #708 Blended, 19½"..............................$350.00-450.00
5. Florane, late line, 12"............................$125.00-150.00
Bottom:
1. Bushberry, 20½"...................................$500.00-600.00
2. Sunflower, 20½"...............................$1,000.00-1,500.00
3. Dogwood II, 19½"..................................$350.00-450.00

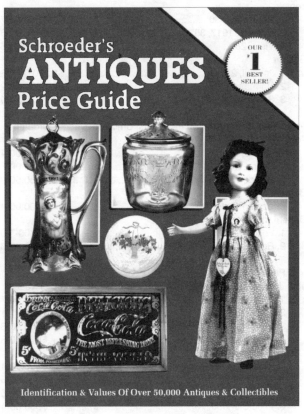